BUILD

UNIVERSES

Nnamso Okon Ekpenyong

Humans shall be free

ISBN 9791220117074
First edition: November 2023

Humans shall be free

To the victims who, under the sway of superior manipulative beings, suffer the consequences of footsteps ordered by superior forces

'No war consumes a race, the war against the human race will not be an exception.

Quote by Dr. Nnamso Okon

The writer is like a soldier: one with thoughts, the other with swords. While you and I sleep, the soldier is out there in the wild, warding off danger. So does the writer: while you sleep, he delves into the abyss of mysteries'

Quote by Dr. Nnamso Okon

REFLECTION

Satan is waging war against God and the hosts of heavens. What gives him the audacity? An instrument of necessity, a useful tool, an agency is tolerated and bolstered by the assigned role of leading the deformed to the place that is prepared for them?

Humans are limited, subjects to higher powers, swayed by superior spiritual beings, captives in torment, living in fear of death yet endowed with freedom of choice - the paradox of the servitor-superior inter-relationship, like the wife that is free to choose to submit or not to her husband.

In the war between Evil and Good, humans are the losers, targets and collaterals. Humans must carry their crosses daily. Changes and war are against humans. Will they ever be free?

HISTORY

Conceived in 1988 and written in 1989, but just like the Prince of Persia tries to wipe out the nation of Israel, the publication of HUMANS SHALL BE FREE like the HEAVENLY MESSENGER was obstructed for decades, not until Prince Michael in *Professor Blessing Abhulimhen-Iyoha* helped.

This is another evidence of the adversary's time being limited and subject to God's permission and the time God set for accomplishing His perfect will. This formula for Freedom or Redemption song or key to preservation survives to the audience as yet another evidence of the hierarchical nature of power:

Even among the celestial princes is the Chiefest.
Amongst the stars in a solar system is the Sun,
Amongst the oceans, is the deepest, and
Besides the gods, is the Highest, the supreme God.
The unlimited, ultimate ALMIGHTY power.
The commander-in-chief
Of the unified cosmic forces in the human milleu,
And so, the only true God who saw to, and triumphed in this dramatization of the scriptures through easily digestible narrations/Dialogue.

INTRODUCTION

"Let there be...", God commanded, and there was. But God then said: "Let us make mankind...", and the Lord God formed man from dust and breathed into his nostrils the breath of life and... man became a living soul.

How these same Humans - the handiwork of God, specially and wonderfully made, in His image and after His likeness, with dominion over earthly creatures - became captives of the fear of the terror of the night and the arrow that flies by day and the pestilence that stalks in darkness and the plague that destroys at midday and the lion, roaming about, looking for whom to destroy, and even the punishment of the wicked unto death is inexplicable except in recourse to the knowledge of the purpose of the human-kind project - the original intention - a blueprint that is on auto-pilot, a process that is unfolding, a work-in-progress that is evolving and getting done over time, ultimately ending in segregation and transpositioning of the perfect (morphed) and the damnable (demorphed) to their respective destinations.

All - as set out in this exposé, HUMANS SHALL BE FREE - laying bare how the spirit-kind manipulates the vulnerable unmarried woman, open to indiscriminate attacks, the drivers of marriage imperatives which also bring on her metamorphosis to the safely secured wife, free from harassment, spared indiscriminate violations, exclusively in her husband's exploitation but fully protected in marriage.

The spirit-kind then uses this metamorphosis from an unmarried woman in peril to a bride, then to a wife - used exclusively by her husband but unendangered and preserved, to actuate, testify, teach, induce, and ensure the morphing from the vulnerability of humans - as captives

15

in torment and fear of death - in the hands of the gods, to the safety of humanity in divinity, as 'the redeemed', in oneness, and rapturing and transporting same to preservation in a destination of shared destiny; while, like the unmarried women, unmorphed humans (designated or induced) crash into eternal doom in fulfillment of the words of promises. The original intention.

The algorithm for deciphering the turn of events concerning the fate of humankind is embedded in the HUMAN-KIND PROJECT, the instrumentality for showcasing the hierarchy of power. It is the calligraphed triumph of the Highest Power (husband, good) over the gods (violators, and evil) using humans: for this very reason - to shew in thee my power, and to proclaim My name - have I raised you. (Ex.9^{16})

So, whether a Moses - turned into a god to show the quality of Love and Mercy, or a Pharaoh - destroyed to showcase power, the purpose of every being's lot is just to showcase awe-inspiring power cruising, bruising, or blessing on the cavalcade of loaded blushing blossoms of Glory (the cruise of power). Beyond that, apart from being dust, you are either one person's trash or another person's treasure in the bin of history - lives and histories, campaigns and guideposts to lead or mislead others to their destination. The sole purpose of this cruise of power is to campaign to sway humans - sojourners in procession - to their destination (promised land or slaughter slab.)

Fallen from the original pedestal of dominion to the fate of protection for women only in the hands of husbands, mirroring that of humanity only in the hands of Divinity, the bruising and blessing by blushing blossoms of power, then the inkling of the procession to a destination of preservation or perdition, an omen, a guidepost that Engenders hunger for a new dimension of existence in freedom.

This desire for Freedom within the bounds of protection, safety, and preservation brings forth an intense desire for a relationship and dependence on the supreme power that becomes a new way, the only Way.

This new awareness - paradoxically, the consciousness that to be free, safe, and happy, women must be under their husbands and humans under God, this knowledge which surpasses all understanding also activates PEACE and actuates hope in the minds of human beings, bringing about a NEWNESS and a need that inspires women to seek refuge in the hands of husbands, the physical manifestation of the spiritual impetus propelling humans to seek salvation in God - crystallizing into a renewal of the mind, banking on spirituality, a rethinking rebranded 'born-againism' or becoming new creatures - former perspectives fading away as old ways are made anew.

Old ways - the original intention - revived by the spirit-kind acting through the lives of Rose and Rhahaab, as it does other human beings, to convince women that they can only be preserved under men, as a lesson to convince humans that they can only be preserved under (in) God.

Created!

With dominion thrust upon him, then, outmaneuvered to fall to dependency, tilling and scratching barren ground, laboring and sweating, bringing forth offspring to mope and grope in darkness, nay scope and gaze through crystal ball a future glazed with uncertainty, reprobates, cast-aways that elope with other gods, nope, cope and hope, doped with fear and wings roped and clipped, to hunt like grasshopper hopping from grass to grass, some like grain jumping from frying pan to fire, the hunter becoming the hunted till benevolent Grace will appear, and lift from grass to Grace the sojourner in fear and hope, captive of death, prospecting for a land flowing with milk, honey, Freedom and preservation.

All as set from the beginning:

The dramatization of THE DEVOLUTION FROM DOMINION TO DEPENDENCY, tactically done to rear and train the craving for redemption, and breed a longing for perfection, a yearning for protection and preservation. To signpost the need for emancipation and achieve the evolution of redemption of 'the lost' onto salvation and the 'irredeemably lost' onto incineration, with justification by the duplexity but oneness of purpose of the spirit-kind. Created, then lost; 'the lost' is redeemed, the irredeemably lost is incinerated.

When you get to your destination, can you then blame the gods for taking you there? You have been warned adequately; besides the lives, histories, campaigns and guideposts: the prophets were all killed as testimonies of your obstinacy - choosing your destination or not heeding the warning. Only to that extent are you the architect of your destiny!

The knowledge that gives Freedom is in Humans shall be free. The key that opens the eyes of understanding and gives the insight that sets the captives free also proves that we are swayed to our destination by the gods even supposing we have choices.

THE AUTHOR'S INSIGHT INTO HUMANITY IN
THE HAND OF DIVINITY
(The threesome game of the gods)

The Conflict in the realm above manifests as Conflict in the realm below.

It is an axiomatic truth that the spirit-kind is bi-faceted. One facet is caring, loving, preserving and fellowshiping - the Highest, the other, wrathful and devouring - the gods. These are unseen opposing superior extraterrestrial forces. The gods scramble for the control of human existence which is exclusively in the hands of Divinity - including in Eternity.

The TRINITY of the beings: humans sandwiched between the supreme and supramundane beings is like the skin between the cutting and the grinding edges of the teeth. One cuts to destroy, the other grinds to remould. To both (head or tail), humans, like the skin under the knife, submit, and like butter to the cutlery, yield, then linger on.

The spirit-kind tussles to prod the puppets along the course and path that leads to preset destinations - destruction or preservation - a two-facedness instantiated by the duo of the violator and the husband, both hunger for and exploit women: Miss stress (Mistress), who, having missed the stress of becoming a wife (being exclusively exploitated by her husband) is fated to be indiscriminately defiled by violators. Woman (Miss or Mrs) is to Man (husband and violator) what humankind (male and female) is to the spirit-kind (the power with absolute control over all creation, the Almighty and the powerful chief Evil planner whose plans are allowed or overridden by the Highest).

19

The whole of womankind is the pawn of mankind (the exploiter), the concrete constant reminder, evidence of humankind being the subject and, at the Mercy of the spirit-kind (the manipulator).

Humans, torn between these contrary forces now rebel against the tyranny and magisterial presence of the gods, and nurse the prospect of independence from the gods. The rival facet advances his project of harnessing and appropriating a proportion of humans into his kingdom for eternal consumption as pepper-soup.

With Humanity tugged between the contending forces of Divinity, weaponized intrigues, palpable betrayal and rebellion smelling in the air and a game plan up each party's sleeve, the stage is set for explosion - the trinity of beings with triunity of projects and trilogy of manoeuvres heading for triumvirate implosion - trine cataclysm of independence of humanity from the gods, rulership of a kingdom that includes some humans by the Devil and supreme rulership of all creatures by the Highest, the original intention.

Armed with the surprise of ambushment, the Highest plays his game close to his chest while a war of supremacy reigns in the celestial realm between the antagonistic forces of the gods with humans trapped and suffering collateral damage. On the final day, while armistice is expected to be declared and a treaty of independent existence of dichotomous parallel kingdoms of the gods is in the works and the Devil is expecting to celebrate his new kingdom with some humans as subjects and humans are anticipating celebrating their independence from the gods, the Highest launches his operation perfection - a project in which He sweeps imperfect humans and all the gods into a well of burning fire to burn to ashes, while He reigns supreme - plans he laid out before the foundations of the Earth , far too overwrought for his opponent to second guess. He then immortalizes flawless humans as his sons and heirs to his perfect kingdom and gives them crowns as rewards (certificate of occupancy as landlords) - another plan up his sleeve, conceived before the foundation of the Earth which was also hidden from his enemies - but unwrapped as perfect kingdom ruled by the most High (evolution of contaminated creation into flawlessness) - new heaven and new Earth - the original intention.

Even with all their shenanigans, intrigues and betrayals, the Highest still dribbles the gods - were the triads of beings, triune of projects and triple apocalypses together with the trio of carrot and stick for Humanity also prearranged - like the Fate of humans? All the same, as actualized, in this moment of epiphany, the original intention was: all creatures are for His pleasure (entertainment) - whether from heaven or from the pit of burning fire - the choice is yours - to glorify Him from Heaven or from Hell.

This throuple is consensual, committed, communicative but do they decide together? Humanity is partitioned between the supreme being and the supramundane being in a threesome game of the beings: the victor wins, the foe is vanquished, and humanity is shared - the final conquest is the second death to prove the law of evolution of creation.

PREAMBLE
HUMANS ARE CAPTIVES TO THE HIERARCHY OF POWER

What is the PURPOSE of the terror of the night and the arrow that flies by day and the pestilence that stalks in darkness and plagues that destroys at midday and the lion, roaming about, looking for whom to destroy, the cankerworms, caterpillars, locusts EXCEPT to chase and torment humans to effectuate their craving for protection under their creator? The instrumentality for establishing and showcasing the hierarchy of power?

What has been prearranged and foreordained is that to escape being devoured by a Supramundane being, humans must embrace protection under the creator. It takes sin (the falling away, freedom, wandering) and its consequences to convince humans of the need for their protection by the creator (Salvation).

The armies of cankerworms, locusts, palmar worms, caterpillars and lions roaming about, seeking whom to destroy were created (prearranged) to torment and so instruct the understanding of humans of the need for their protection by the creator.

A prearranged and preordained practical example humans can see, learn from and be instructed by is that to escape indiscriminate violations, women must embrace the protection of marriage.

Similarly, it takes feminism and divorce to convince women of this parallel axiom - that they can only escape indiscriminate defilement by violators under a husband -

all appointed and decreed unto hapless humans - the tri-une of husband, wife and violators mirrors the creator, the devil and human triunity. This is demonstrated by this short story.

A married woman had eleven consecutive pregnancies which ended in habitual abortions. She had no child. Nothing to show for years of marriage, for which reason her husband taunted her, insinuated he married a man or a barren woman and threatened to divorce her and marry a fruitful woman.

Her aunty had taken her to countless hospitals, native doctors, prayer houses and solution grounds, all without result. On this particular day, this same auntie this time around took her to the most popular pastor in town, for deliverance. They first waited for their turn, amongst many people with problems, in the reception, to see the pastor.

In the interval between when he finished with one client and when another one entered, the pastor, from over work, slept off. In that slumber, he dreamt that a goat, with a rope tied round its neck, was dragged by a woman into his presence. The attitude of the woman, coupled with her mannerism and the way she pushed and shoved her prisoner, the goat, into his presence woke the pastor from his nap.

This coincided with when the auntie and her niece were ushered into his office.

PASTOR (led by the spirit, to the auntie):
-What has this young woman done to you to justify your putting her through all these pain and travail? (Pointing to the woman in need of his intercession).

AUNTIE (Submissively, to the pastor):
-The one who sees what others do not see. I will confess. The one with the powers of the spirits. I will confess. The one that receives information hidden from ordinary mortals from above. I will confess.

PASTOR (Peremptorily):
-Confess right now or the fire of the power of the anointing that I carry will consume you.

AUNTIE (hesitating, then grimly):
-My junior sister, the mother of this my niece, dared me when we were girls, married before me and had children before me. That provoked me. So, I promised her children would pay for her audacity.

PASTOR (wincing, aghast at her cruelty):
-Just that indiscretion? Only that incaution moved you to buffet your innocent niece with eleven miscarriages, childlessness and turbulent marriage?

AUNTIE (Switching to the mode of aridity):
-My sister dared me. When she dared the lion, rode and made jamboree atop the lion's back, what did she expect? No human dares the initiated, no one pokes fun at those of us with powers over others and goes unscathed.

PASTOR (As if he has recovered from the initial shock, inquisitively):
-So, what exactly did you do to your niece?

AUNTIE (without any feelings):
-I drank the blood of her pregnancies and ate her babies.

PASTOR (in another level of horror, then, curiously):
-Who gave you such powers?

AUNTIE (enigmatically):
-Humans who are initiated into the agency of the supernatural are given powers from the spiritual realm with which they carry out assignments on behalf of superior beings against targeted humans. Pastor (reverently), I can discern that your own power is greater than mine. The source of your power must be greater than mine. There are realms and there are powers, levels, authorities and principalities and there are beings and beings. I had to confess to be free from the searing heat, from the fire of your power because your power is far above mine. Life exists in levels. And, as water has levels, power has levels too. I see you, far above, sitting at the right-hand side of the Highest with all other powers under your feet. I fear you. I tremble in your presence. (Already writhing in pains).

PASTOR (shouts as if he is possessed):
-I command you, in the name that is above all names, by the power that is above all powers, by the blood of the Lamb, release your captive from bondage this minute. Release her from torment immediately. Set her free now!

AUNTIE (falls, shaking, trembling and still writhing in pains):
-It is done! She is free! I set her free, now. She is free. Please, spare me. Do not destroy me with the fire of your power.

Nine months from that day, the niece delivered a bouncing baby boy and her husband treated her as a darling wife from that day. And, on the day of the naming-

26

ceremony of the baby, the same pastor that interceded for the baby's mother's barrenness, this time around on invitation, came; the same auntie with supra-human powers who thwarted the baby's mother's fruitfulness, uninvited, also came. The pastor was surprised to see her, but she was not.

Dramatically, the auntie knelt, bowed and kissed the pastor's feet. In addition, she submitted:

-Pastor, you are great! Your power is greater!

But we all get our powers from the same spiritual kingdom. Why is your power superior to mine?

The Pastor was shocked.

-In the spiritual kingdom, there is a hierarchy of power, there is a power, far and above all other powers, the ultimate power. All powers belong to Him, and he gives it to whom he chooses - he intoned.

The Auntie agreed.

-On earth, all humans have equal power except those with powers gained from super-natural sources. I came to declare that your power is indeed superior. I came to submit to your power and to ask for forgiveness from my niece. Everyone at the ceremony was surprised at this effusive public display of confession, repentance and audacity.

The pastor then asked her: -How did you come by this your power?

She replied eagerly: -In exactly the same way you got yours.

-I got my powers by accepting that my Lord is Lord and saviour of all - the pastor explained.

-Just that? I have accepted that too. So, am I now as powerful as you are? - she asked, half sarcastic and half confused.

-Not exactly so. Believe, accept and conform to and do the will of the Almighty. The level of your power is according to your faith, you can grow in your faith and so grow your power - the pastor explained further.

The auntie, more stupefied than Enlightened, asked:

-Where can I get faith from? Does fate give faith?

-Spiritual things come from conviction rather than by physical proof - the pastor added.

-I am convinced your power is overriding (she bows again), give me your power, I have thrown away my power. Your power is above mine, and my power is above human power; so, I am better off with your kind of power - she said, maintaining her intransigence.

At his wit's end, the pastor asked: -How exactly did you acquire your power, or how did you get initiated?

Reluctantly, she narrated her life story.

-My mother had only two of us in a polygamous setting where envy and rivalry was rife. For us to survive the wiles and intricacies of polygamous life, she had to seek our protection from wizardry. She mentioned her need for protection to her friend who introduced her to witchcraft. But on joining them, she noticed that in their meetings, turn by turn, members used to compulsorily offer their children as sacrificial lambs in exchange for extraordinary power. These lambs ritualistically used to be roasted, shared and eaten by members in orgies of celebrations, at the end of which the child would die in real life. It was not long before it dawned on my mother that the search for protection landed her where it would soon be her turn to offer her children as sacrifice. And it was too late for her to back out. Any such attempt would earn her death. So, from the outset, she never ate her share of the sacrifice. Then came her turn.

Her members demanded she donated me as their sacrifice. She refused on the grounds that it was my protection that drove her into the cult. "How can she kill the child that she joined the cult to protect?" - she asked the colleagues. "You ate other people's children and want your children protected?" - they queried her.

-You can only get protection from the Lord of Lords and the King of Kings, the apex of power, protection cannot come from any other source. Protection and ultimate power come from my Lord - interjected the pastor.

She ignored the pastor and continued with her story.

-Her colleagues made mountain out of her refusal to offer me as sacrifice. They said she had no option except she returned her portion of other members children she ate - wrongly believing she ate her share and could not reproduce any part thereof. They made storm out of her refusal to sacrifice her children. They threatened to kill my mother. As their final rite of conviction, they danced around her and sang this song:

"NOTHING GOES FOR NOTHING.
BLOOD FOR POWER.
NOTHING GOES FOR NOTHING.
BLOOD FOR PROTECTION.
NOTHING GOES FOR NOTHING.
BLOOD FOR BLOOD.
NOTHING GOES FOR NOTHING
OBEDIIENCE FOR SALVATION".

At the point they wanted to kill my mother, she produced her portion of other members' children who were sacrificed explaining that because she did not want her children sacrificed, she did not partake in eating other members' children.

The pastor, recovering from the rapture by the spell her story cast on him, said: -I did not sacrifice anything before I got my powers.

-Pastor, you did - answered the woman spontaneously.

-Pastor, remember the blood of the Lamb? There is power in the blood.

-That was sacrificed by the Father - defended the pastor.

-Sacrifice is sacrifice, blood is blood, whether by the Father or the mother, something must be sacrificed for something - she insisted.

The pastor was instructed: somebody paid for the mercies he savoured and the power he exercised. He still asked:

-How exactly did you get initiated?

She continued her story. -The only option that could make them spare my mother's life was her acceptance to initiate me into their cult in place of sacrificing me.

The pastor still insisted. -So, how exactly did she initiate you?

-My mother laced my food with her portion of other members' children they killed which she refused to eat but safe-kept.

The pastor asked further: -So, when you ate that food, did you turn to a witch?

She added: -The night I ate that food, my spirit was summoned to their meeting where the initiation was completed.

-So, do they have the power to summon human spirit? - asked the pastor.

-They have the power to cast spell on their victims, the power to turn to bats and fly, to curse people and they invoke supernatural powers and use it to control other people and they can take the souls of their victims and keep them in their coven, thus causing the death of such persons - she narrated effusively.

-But they and their source of power are still under the power of the Almighty - the pastor added.

-So, the source of your power and the source of my power all work in unison, in tandem to achieve their purpose. Superior power works in conjunction with the supreme power on humans, as in their design, you and I are the ones ordinary humans can see, relate with and be instructed that if as intermediaries our delegated powers can bind and unbind, then the powers of the invisible spiritual beings can make or mar, and those whom the stronger had bound can be loosed from their bond by the strongest. The substantiation of the existence of the spirit-kind is the enormous potency of their delegated power which we exercise in the physical on ordinary humans like my niece in the organogram of power. No one sees the air but everyone feels the action of air - branches of trees swayed and roots of trees uprooted by the power of the wind (air in motion); so do humans not see the spirits but feel the extraordinary potency of their power. The spirit beings prove their existence through the intermediaries - you cannot see them, so you doubt their existence, but you see what they do by the hands of the intermediaries and the Earthquake they wrought about, so you believe they exist and submit to the supreme power.

The purpose of humans is to see, experience, feel, appreciate and declare the existence of the spirit-kind as expressed in their actions. Spiritual beings do not flog humans with cane as punishment nor use guns, munitions and explosives to destroy them instead they employ human agencies and delegate powers to created elements to war against humans. Humans are the instantiation of the spirits and the substantiation of their power - she concluded.

PROLOGUE
HUMANITY AND DIVINITY

The highest laid the foundations of the Earth, the gods set the world upon the pillars of the Earth, and Divinity made and settled humanity to sojourn in it, in unison, did they also determine and set on autopilot the order and footsteps of human beings and whatever eventually each human being turns out to be.

At their whims, are some women turned to wives and others are never so; some women are made mothers, some are never so; some humans are born males, some as females berthed; each allotted Time, Space and Path, that is par for the course.

Some they bless, smile upon, or grant whatever their heart desires, and bestow good will, unusual, uncommon, unrivalled intelligence on, then steer to succeed; others they harden their hearts and frustrate to fail, so that some will forever live while others will die. So does the deity drill (preside over) humanity along the path of freedom that leads to preservation – proving the law of preservation: that only in the Highest is Humanity preserved and genuine human freedom is anchored in Him alone.

This is the predicament that humanity is up against: Humanity in the hands of Divinity - dependent - at their mercy, and, hoping, some day to be free from or surmount; contending with having his footsteps ordered by Divinity and his Fate determined, future controlled and affairs presided over by the deity and driven by delusions of bondage in the hands of the gods and, drunken by the desires of fake perditious freedom from the law of pilgrimage: the sojourner is dependent on the goodwill of the host.

Can the sojourner then contend with the host? Can the creature contest with his creator? Can humanity escape the control of Divinity: will humans ever be free? Free from having to choose between the freedom that leads to perdition and the freedom that leads to preservation when his choice is on a remote controller? Free to choose, but the choice is remote controlled?

HUMANITY IN THE HANDS OF DIVINITY
(a threesome game of the gods):

INTRODUCTION

Women are made weaker and the weapons of indiscriminate violations, harassment and attacks by all men fashioned against them so as to generate in them the craving for the protection offered by marriage just as weapons of warfare are fashioned against humans to make them hunger for protection under the Highest; just as it took torments by their slave masters for the Israelites to turn to their God.

The conflict in the spirit realm manifests as the conflict in the realm below:

CAST:
HUMAN BEINGS
(THE GHOST OF) ROSALINDA, ALEXANDA
AMANDA
SUPRAMUNDANE BEING
SUPREME BEIN

ACT ONE. SCENE ONE

What purpose do the gods have for humans except to be tools for their purpose?

The atmosphere is dense, sombre, solemn and uncertain. We see the lawful captives: ROSALINDA, ALEXANDA and AMANDA, before their second death, as they are led to the well of burning fire. On the brink of the well, ALEXANDA protests that because of the fresh evidence, he is appealing against their conviction. This stalls the eternal condemnation of their souls.
Whilst their accuser-cum-prosecutor, their legal captor balks at such an idea, then coasts down the well of burning fire, as if that is his natural abode; the trio remains in the boundary between the blissful and blastful eternity zones.

ROSALINDA (while awaiting the final verdict, in this wilderness of hope, despondently):
-Why are humans passed through this harrowing furnace: gestation, birth, life, death, then second death? Just to turn them into gold or charcoal? The gestation is a gamble, oftentimes ends in abortion, the first stage of the culling of humans in the stepwise reduction of the candidates for the next selection exercise.

His birth is in pains: squeezed through a narrow tunnel. At birth, in shock and expressing dismay and the helpless plight of its sudden appearance in a battlefield, it cries after grasping. To breathe he must labour. To excrete he must strain, in sleep he will snore, to swallow he will chew, to live he must respire after perspiring, to feed he must hunt, oftentimes consumed in his hunt - prey to countless predators. Must the passage of humans through the fire of gestation, birth, life and death necessarily

37

precede the ultimate selection for salvation? Could they not have been created saved or the fallen saved without the incineration?

Humans who survive the birth and gestational herd culls are further, daily buffeted by diseases, battered by disasters, pounded by harsh environment, afflicted by severe weather, pelted by other elements, darted by unseen forces and frustrated by unfathomable obstacles.

His miserable life, depicted, even scripturally, is in trepidation and afflictions of the terror of night and the arrow that flies by day and the pestilence that stalks in darkness and the plague that destroys at midday and the lion, roaming about, looking for whom to destroy, till he dies in suffocation. In asphyxiation he is birthed, in suffocation he exits as awaiting-conflagration, who has allowed this, even purposed it, even though he is a subject-cum-Prince of Divinity.

This survivor of asphyxiation that exited in suffocation still has an after-life of tribulations - even though this subject-cum-prince of Divinity has a benevolent guardian Deity. Who has purposed this?

AMANDA (in the wilderness of fantasied hope, crest-fallen):

From same ore, is smelted gold, and its other extract is charred to charcoal. Their fate, unchangeable fate. Sealed fate. This is what Providence designed and set in place.

Who is greater than our creator? What is more evil than the devil? What surpasses this direst predicament? We are tugged between the two sides of the spirit-kind - one facet offers preservation, in his wrath, the other offers annihilation, we are between the devil and our maker, between good and evil, cold and heat, between life and death, peace and suffering. Poor humans, carry your crosses, the cross of humankind is the battle for their soul by the spirit-kind - the goodness and the wrathful form (consuming fire) of the same kind. One purpose, one - kind, one entity, multiple forms.

What do they need humans for? Did they jointly make humans for them to harvest, thresh, sieve into granary or cull by winnowing into fire? As dolls are toys to babies, are humans playthings to the spirits? Or did they create humans to compulsorily serve them eternally in their freedom? For their set end, in unison, the bi faceted spirit-kind has purposed this.

Why the contestation over eternal ownership of human- kind? What do the spirits prey on humans for? Is human blood an aperitif that satiates their desire? Is Human suffering, their digestiff? Is Human flesh, their only nourishment? Human soul, the only booster-dose for their essence? Is Human spirit, the trophy for their spirit? Does human essence salve their ego? For basking in human worship and feasting on human praises, Humankind must depend on spirit-kind?

Or because human heart is the only temple for their habitation that human eternity should be the merest judgment-debt for the pretext of mere disobedience? Or is it just for humans to be servitors to spirits? Or because the doll is a child's toy, so should humans be puppets of the spirit-kind? Can't the spirit-kind do without Humankind? With every iota of humans being the ingredients for the living salad of the spirit-kind - Will humans ever be free? For their set end, in unison, the spirit-kind has purposed this. Will this warfare by unseen forces in the heavenly realm against blood and flesh ever end?

ALEXANDA (the de jure superiority of the spirit-kind vis-à-vis the lot of humankind as well as the concept of the right of narcissism overriding Mercy and loving kindness suddenly struck him, insightfully):

This running battle is to fence humans from the power of doing whatever they purpose to do, power that is exclusive to the gods - humans are to be consigned to worshiping and serving the spirit kind, instead of having their eyes opened lest they are as gods.

Many are the afflictions of humans. So also, are their battles: the war to shut the gates of the Garden of knowledge against humans - lest they extract knowledge (the basis of this Power) and live according to human terms - instead of living as tools of the gods. So also, were they crushed by the great flood, subdued by the diversifying of human tongues (unity of purpose) and brought to their knees to force submission to the spirit kind as wives submit to their husbands and by their being scattered upon the face of the Earth - all to stop humans from gaining this power to escape limitation. The war to darken human understanding, veil the eyes of their Understanding, maintain delegable power differential and contain the indomitable human spirit by the diametric spirit-kind.

Should the template of power war in the realm above be duplicated in the realm below? Should humans be set on the template of power war and fear of the hour of reckoning? Who allowed, even purposed this? Puppet or pawn in the threesome game of power is decipherable from this eye-opening Yoruba proverb which aptly captures human predicament thus: wheresoever fate leads one to, that's the path one takes.

Or more succinctly put, whatsoever has been purposed by Providence for each human to pass through in life is what they pass through. Simply understood as, whatever befalls a man in this life, even in the life-after-death, is his lot - what has been foisted on him by the power that has absolute control over human affairs.

(He stands in the land of the Great Beyond, mesmerised, gazing afar and ruminating on the nature of existence. The Great Riddle of Life and afterlife):

(intuitively):

It now dawns on me that only by the segregation and assignment of humans into defiant (evil, Pharooh) and submissive (good, Israel) beings and leading them as the 'saved' and the 'lost' to their reckoning and reward can the entertainment and glory of the spirit-kind be full, the plight of the unfortunate human beings notwithstanding. Superiority vis-a-vis inferiority is on display in the plight of humanity.

As enunciated by the great teacher" ... but this happens (...this man suffers blindness) so that the works of God might be displayed in him.

ROSE:

-What a human being is to the spirit-kind is what the ball is in a field of play. Just as the ball is tossed, hit, kicked, headed, used to dribble the opponents to convince the spectators and the contenders of the prowess, skills and the superiority of the best player, regardless of what happens to the ball, so is a human being tossed for the amusement of the spirit kind, regardless of how hurt, broken or destroyed the human being is.

After all: the clay is in the hands of the potter. Narcissism is stellar than empathy. The inferior is at the Mercy of the superior. The natural is subject to the supernatural.

Humankind is visible but the spirit kind is invisible, and the spirit kind is invincible but humankind is

41

vincible. Human being: alone he came, alone he stands, abandoned even by his shadow in the dark labyrinth of reckoning, overwhelmed, facing the hosts of the spiritual realm. Human experiences are mirrors reflecting these attributes of the spirit kind - so what is human suffering when power is at play? The position of humans in the hierarchy of power: the receiving end. Savour whatever is thrust on you.

The spirit-kind revels in showcasing his glory by the doom or the recompence of humankind. This is the sole purpose of the plight of humankind. Show pieces are preserved in show glasses, but humans are used as show pieces without regard for their preservation.

The albatross of humankind is the exhibition of power by the spirit kind - the inferiorization of humankind for the proclamation of the superiority of the spirit kind through adversity which wakens human senses and tragedy which jolts humans into submission.

Humankind in the hands of the Spirit-kind. The Human-cum-spirit ecosystem - the ecosystem of the BE-INGS is a marketplace for bartering favours for obeisance, retribution for disobedience - altruism does not operate here.

AMANDA (hopelessly):
-Life - as pre-set, happens to us. We are what life makes us to be, life's plan for us, mere miserable humans, all beset with troubles, burdened, wearied, brow beaten and harnessed to our yoke - merely doing our Time.

As the flocks are fed and fattened for their wool - the purpose of their creation, and women are beautified and purposed to be mere treadmill for testing manliness - the prowess of men, and Israel and Pharaoh were chosen and used to demonstrate the rescuing plus destroying Power

42

of God, so are all humans created for use in showcasing the powers of the gods.

Humans are harassed, humiliated, harnessed and subjugated; like the potter's power over the clay, of the same lump is predestined and justified vessels that yield or are subdued, humbled and made meek and shepherded to their recompense and vessels of wrath, explicitly prepared as lamb to the slaughter, designated for the Day of Massacre, all to proclaim the praises of the power and purpose of Mercy to the elect.

All the ado (gestation, birth, life, and death) is about humans bowing to power, sorting out humans who bend or do not bend to the will of the gods. Human culling or evolution, dubbed salvation of the souls, selecting and equiping the saints for the work of service, so the abiding saints can be fully harnessed.

Some are created vessels for service, those who fail in this regard are lumped with vessels created, then, fitted for destruction, to be massacred on an appointed day, both ways proclaiming the powers of the agency of the gods as are the justification of the ungodly and the bringing of the dead to life in Christ - everything has been pre-programmed to happen to proclaim the ultimate POWER.

Good, vessels of Mercy or Evil, vessel of wrath (both lives are in the hands of the spirit kind) as mirrors reflecting, revealing, declaring the POWER of the gods, so humans will live in awe of the spirit-kind.

Curtain falls.

ACT ONE. SCENE TWO

Humankind is under the control of the spirit-kind: all are created specced to purpose, each spec coaxed, lured, tricked, frustrated, forced by circumstances or convinced to lead a life that is a mirror, a lesson, a usable tool that leads or misleads others to the place (at the right or left hand side, in heaven or hell) that has been prepared for them.

Same atmosphere: dense, tense, solemn, sombre and pervasive uncertainty. The trio is, after an interlude, seen at the temple of Justice. We see, in the Divine court, the Judge that is burning like a fiery flame, but consuming nothing, on an elevated platform, draped in imperial splendour and, seated, decked in majesty and excellency, on the judgment throne that is shimmering, the judge, in garment as white as snow, the hair of his head as pure as wool, confident, arrayed with glory and beauty, in full regalia, glorious, glowing, so sparkling and radiant that we are not comfortable looking in the direction of the judgment seat.

A book of record of works, opened, hung like a wall-mirror and facing the appellants is conspicuously displayed, with the records of the appellants highlighted. And the book of life is similarly displayed.
Below the elevated platform stands the trio, downcast, powerless, penitent, sober, in sombre mood, and condemned to an eternity of damnation.

HUMAN BEING (the ghost of ALEXANDA, pointing to ROSALINDA):
-Since this woman you gave to me secured her freedom from me, I came to you to procure my freedom.

45

SUPREME BEING (unmoved):
-Humans are free only when they wholly trust their creator. Then will they be free from fear, captivity, and free from death.

ALEXANDA:
-Not freedom imprisoned by trust, nor with strings attached, neither freedom based on dependency, but being free, as free as the air, independent, or not relying on another being.

SUPREME BEING:
-Does the air you said is free not obey the commander of its direction? Submit to your God, surrender to your Maker, obey your creator, do his will and be at peace, and that will set you free with all other things added unto you. If the moth seeks out for and gravitates towards the flame, should humans seek independence and separation from their creator? The freedom of humans emanates from dependency.

ALEXANDA:
- Freedom that is subsumed in submission, or entangled in dependence, or in exchange for services, and flowing from obligation is tantamount to "nothing goes for nothing" or independence in dependence.

SUPREME BEING:
-Do you prefer freedom to life in eternity that is shone by the glory of the Highest and set in the celestial realm? Will you jettison living in a celestial community of saints, a place of peace, rest, love, and worship for freedom? Will you abandon living in mansions in Heaven that are brilliant like jasper, clear as crystal with streets paved with gold for freedom?

Will you opt for freedom instead of sharing God's glory, strength, authority and blessings? Will you choose freedom over being heir to God's inheritance? Can an infant be free from parental restrictions without consequences? Can a baby be safely free from the mother's breast milk? Can a child make it without the parents' instructions? Is it safe? Is freedom safe, without dare consequences?

My thoughts toward you are thoughts of good, my plan for you is that of life of bliss in a place far above all tormentors, that is freedom indeed, perfect freedom, complete freedom with peace and rest guaranteed.

If freedom is what seems right to you, note that its path leads to destruction, its way is the way of damnation, its history is that of condemnation, the idea smacks of rebellion, and is a subject of confrontation, its originators are usually accused of envy, and being contenders with the Almighty, its conception is shrouded in confusion, its appeal is the lure of the devil, its birth is from the womb of the evil one, it is berthed by Satan himself, its end is that of perdition, like the fly attracted to the coffin, drawn by the stench of the corpse: such a fly must also share the destiny of the corpse.

SUPRAMUNDANE BEING: (peevish, lanky, shadowy, scary, feathery, out-of-this worldly, clad in torn, charred, worn-out attire, with miniature unequal wings that aid it, like Tse Tse-fly, dart about - uninvited, reappears, interjects, points to ALEXANDA):

-He ate the forbidden fruits, from the tree of knowledge and the tree of freedom and unchecked, he will also eat the fruit from the tree of life.
I am the witness, I and only I, put aside this ethereal incorporeality, met his companion face to face, inoculated

her with deceptiveness and the prowess of seduction, gave the fruits, first to her; she ate it first and then gave it to him. He ate the fruit from the tree in the centre of the garden.

From that moment, his eyes opened, he became wise, he gained insight, his horizon widened, and with his heart seethed with envy, he sought invisibility, invincibility and immortality, the exclusive entitlements of superior beings.

From the day they tasted the forbidden fruits, they became rebellious, they sought independence from spiritual control and desired equality with superior beings in power and wisdom.

He conceived in his heart to be like us, his transmundane beings: incorporeal, creative, free, manipulative. That is a great sin to conceive in his heart to be like us. That is a coup de grace against his superior beings. And the penalty is death. Hence, the pre-emptive arrest and captivity.

(Pointing to all of them now):
   -And so, they are my legal captives.

ALEXANDA:
-Did you also infuse my companion with wickedness and deviousness?

SUPRAMUNDANE BEING:
-That is not why we are here now.

SUPREME BEING (Directing this to the SUPRA-MUNDANE BEING):
-Were you there when I laid the foundations of the earth or when I fastened the force of gravity on the earth and hung the earth upon nothing? Do you know how I spread the molten glass-like sky over the earth? Do you

know from whose womb come daylight and darkness? Out of whose womb comes ice or snow?

Were you there when the pillars of the heavens were erected over the earth? Or, when the boundaries of the waters with the earth were drawn, were you there?

SUPRAMUNDANE BEING (peevishly, like an enraged advocate, selects his words cautiously):
- But I was there when he ate the forbidden fruits, the fruits from the trees in the centre of the garden. The very fruits that you banned them from touching. The earth was my witness when he committed the iniquity. The earth first shuddered, and then quaked when he committed the abomination. Till date, the Earth still quakes because they did the unthinkable. The sun was shocked in confoundment when transgression was planted in his heart, the moon was stirred from her slumber when sin germinated from the discord sown in the farm of his mind, the firmament was awaken when he plowed iniquity and sowed wickedness and the same was harvested from the plantation of his consciousness, the galaxies were aglow when the pollens of death were reaped and dispersed from the flowers of his spirit. That is why the shooting stars hide their faces in shame whenever his conscience becomes an open wound and an eyesore. And the world was agog when damnation became his only portion. They munched the fruit that you barred them from desiring. That is why they are inevitably my legal captives. That is why they are in my hand.

SUPREME BEING:
-They are my only terrestrial craftsmanship. My handiwork from the dust of the earth. Other terrestrial creatures are the products of my command.

SUPRAMUNDANE BEING (flaming):

-Is that why you have soft-spot for him? Is that why he should become the apple of your eye, the one after your heart? Is that why they should become gods? Is that why they should take over the work of your command: "Multiplying and filling the earth?" Is that why they should do it in the middle of the garden? Even after you banned them from doing it? In the middle of the garden: is that not iniquitous?

SUPREME BEING:

-Before the foundation of the earth, I chose him in Him. When I formed him with the word of my mouth from the dust of the earth, what part did you play?

SUPRAMUNDANE BEING (self-aggrandizing, argumentatively):

-You created humans, I concede without admitting, but I created and installed, in the brief moment of your absence, that software in them, in that part of their mind, that makes them short of your glory, naturally disobedient, rebellious, prone to erring, desperately wicked and incapable of showing love. Any human who disobeys you breaks your covenant with him and automatically enters into covenant with me, to perpetually disobey you, follow me and do my biddings and on my part I will carry the human on my able shoulders to eternity, my own eternity.

Human beings are our tools or our subjects. Our consensus concerning flesh and blood ab initio. You pick some, and I pick others. We manipulate them to our eternities. Then and only then, peace will reign on earth, in Heaven and in the bottom of our hearts. For this service they were set apart before they were formed in their mothers' wombs.

The destiny of human beings is in the hands of spiritual beings. We use them to achieve our expected end. As the bow sends the arrow on errand, in the same way incorporeal beings send corporeal beings. As darts are programmed for shooting, in the same way super-human beings programme human nature. As the tailor fashions the dress of a model, in the same way we design the destinies of human beings. As the branches of trees are swayed by the direction of the wind so are the actions and inactions of humans swayed by the dictates of supernatural beings.

As the computer formats a document, in the same way we format the lives of humans, to give them our expected end. All they have is in our power and they are in our hands.

As we determine when they are born, who is a male and who is a female, to whom they are born, where they are born and when they die, in the same way we order their footsteps and determine where they spend eternity, your or my eternity.

ALEXANDA (interjecting):
-If you created human beings in your own image, with emotions, capacity to feel pain and frustration, but for you to manipulate, control, afflict, and abandoned to be buffeted by forces beyond them, tossed back and forth by the waves, blown side to side by the wind, where is fairness and justice in such arrangement?

SUPRAMUNDANE BEING (annoyed):
-Can the pot dictate to the potter? Does the pot know to what use it will be put or for what purpose it was moulded? Does the pot decide whether it will be put on fire or on ice-block? The clay is in the hands of the potter, to fashion out designs that please his eyes and meet the

needs of his desires. Humans are in the hands of spiritual beings, their superior beings. As the sparks fly upwards to the uncertainty of landing in fire or in safety, so are humans born unto troubles and the uncertainty of ending in bliss or blast. Can flesh and blood battle power and principalities? Can corporeality see and knock out incorporeality? Have you ever seen the shadows of spirits? Do you know why humans were made? Was it not to be messengers, agents, instruments with which spiritual beings achieve their intentions?

ALEXANDA:

-If superior beings order the footsteps of humans, why do humans suffer the punishment of missteps ordered by higher beings?

SUPRAMUNDANE BEING:

-You are a lower being, but endowed with intellect, reasoning, understanding and the power of choice. As you are given shadows, so are your footsteps ordered, but the choice is also given to you to take or not the steps, that is the mystery of being-hood. That is the mystery in the inter-relationship between spirit-kind and human-kind. Ultimately, the freedom of choice is yours.

ALEXANDA:

-Humans do not have freedom from the gods but they have freedom of choice. Is the choice really ours? Can the arrow refuse the errand of the bow? Do the shadows choose what they do? Can the shadow do more than mimic or follow its owner? Like our shadows, do we choose how we are used or how we are bidden to choose? Can sparks stand the heat of the fire? Can the clay say no to the hands of the potter? Can the document deformat the computer? Are scissors in the hands of the cloth? Do branches of trees see the wind or know its direction? Can the parrot fly as high as the eagle? Can flesh and blood, unalloyed, overcome manipulation by principalities and power?

Higher power belongs to higher beings, absolute power is absolutely in their hands. Can humans make un-manipulated or "un-teleguided" choices?

And so, the mandators, the manipulators, the gods are to blame for the missteps of humans and the consequential suffering of the lower beings. The spirit-kind is responsible for the plight of mankind. If not for the hand-work of death, our people say, the dead will not know the grave nor suffer in there. Like death, their weapon, the gods are surely to blame for the predicament of humankind.

SUPREME BEING:

-As I created humans, in the same way I formed the crooked serpent. Nothing was made without me. Everything was made from my command and for my use. Do you know where whirlwind or cold wind comes from? Where rain comes from or on whose counsel cloud forms? My breath brings out frost and as I thunder throughout the whole earth, so do I not seek counsel from anyone. On whose advice is the balancing of the planets on their galaxies? When I set up the arrays of galaxies, where were you?

SUPRAMUNDANE BEING (protesting):

-They are, nonetheless, still my legal captives. Once acquired, the sinful and rebellious nature of humankind is permanent. Can the leopard change its spots? Can the cat stop using its claws or stop purring? Is it not encrypted in their gene? Is it not cast in their marrow? Is sin not ingrained in their nature? Does the soul that sin not die anymore? They broke your laws and smashed the tablets of the covenant between you and them. Remember! You asked them to choose between you and I. Willingly, they chose me.

Remember the agreement: If they depend on you solely, you will carry them on your wings, like the eagle, through your narrow and impossible ways to eternity, and plant them where no one can afflict them anymore. But they feel they are wise, they believe they know what is good for them, they refused to be the clay for the potter's plans, chose to depend on me, trudge with me into my own eternity; simply because I made my way straight and simple. My ways are like their ways: easy to follow.

I am the spiritual police, the accuser, the prosecutor-cum-examiner of humans. If I do not clip their wings, wring their necks and place them where they belong, they will rub shoulders with us and rubbish us, their superior beings. Birds fly, and butterflies fly. So, the butterfly thinks it is a bird. Squirrels glide through the air, does that make them flying animals? Bats fly like birds, does that turn them into birds? Soon, humans will secretly wish they are like us: invincible, invisible, spiritual and immortal; they will see themselves as gods. After all, we are all beings, are of same image. It must not happen because incorporeal beings are transcendental to human beings. (Shaking his head in protest):

- Remember! Agreement is agreement. Your word is your bond. Your word does not return to you void. It must be fulfilled. They have met all the criteria of becoming prisoners by choice, prisoners of the law and unamendable: not keeping covenant, ignorance of their limitations as humans and disobedience. To be free from your high-handedness, they flouted your order, disobeyed you; separated from you they stand, independent of your protection, condemned they are, perish they must. They asked for freedom, freedom to die they have gotten.

SUPREME BEING (disarmingly):
-They are mere humans. It is their nature to err. They are not alien to error. To err is human. Disobedience is not an irredeemable sin. I have a redemption plan for them. I will chastise them with my right hand and cuddle them with the left. I will ransom humankind out of captivity in your hands.

SUPRAMUNDANE BEING (Sarcastically):
-One hand, with pruning shears, chastises, the other, with Mercy, coddles and cossets. One purpose, different ways, same destination: eternity. Your way is too narrow, your ways are not their ways. You can only ransom a handful of them, the mammoth crowd of them will follow me willingly into my own eternity.

SUPREME BEING:
-With me nothing is impossible.

SUPRAMUNDANE BEING (laughing noisily):
-Adam and Eve heard your voice as you spoke to them and fellowshipped with them. But when the chips were down, they disobeyed you, rejected you, and chose to follow me because they trust and believe me; and your way is not their way, it is narrow, rough, slippery, slopy, tortuous and impossible to follow. What new thing will you do to win these prodigal children back to you that you forgot to do in the garden?

SUPREME BEING:

-Now, they will see signs and wonders and have miracles and testimonies that will convince them to depend and rely solely on me and so, do my will.

SUPRAMUNDANE BEING:

-Testimonies greater than the garden with the fullness thereof in spite of which humans choose to be captives in my Kingdom instead of being slaves worshipping you eternally. What will you do this time that will not fail like the flood or the ark?

SUPREME BEING:

-This time around, I will send my son, He will bruise your head and at the mention of his name your knees will bow. He will set the captives free. He will destroy your works and the gates of your kingdom will not prevail against him. Grace will come, and the comforter will come. Now, as they behold my glory, as in a mirror, they will become transformed into my image. I will give them a new nature that will not hunger for you and will not know you. I will feed their new nature with my words, will train and test them until they turn to gold and will not obey you anymore. As I give lightning unto the ends of the earth, in the same way I will give understanding to their spirit: they will loathe you.

This time around, I have given them eternal life and they shall never lose it or perish, and nobody will be able to snatch them out of my hand. Through sacrifice, they will be gained back to their original position.

SUPRAMUNDANE BEING (confidently):

-I have tempted them already. They are not different from the sons of perdition. The sons of perdition are mine: the brides, prepared, adorned, beautified and kept for me. The demons are also in my community.

SUPREME BEING:
-Except of course the sons of perdition, that my words may be fulfilled. Others, set aside before they were formed: you may desire them, you may attack them, you may afflict them, but you cannot snatch them from my hand.

ALEXANDA (interjecting curiously):
-Do you allow and even purpose the suffering of the Elect?

SUPREME BEING:
-They are in this same world, but they are not of this world. He may touch them, but he cannot take them out of my hand. I have set a hedge between Him and them.

SUPRAMUNDANE BEING (hilariously):
-Ha! Ha! Ha! Ha! 'Till then. Ha, ha, ha, ha. 'Till then. When we get to that bridge, crossing will take place. I will work harder, than never before to gather the humans that will worship me in eternity. For that reason, we made humans: human beings are made to serve spiritual beings. Some will be slaves worshipping you, and some will be captives to me.

ALEXANDA (enlightened and emboldened):
-Passing us through gestation, birth, life and death, has it not made us to become superior beings? Have we not yet matured into spiritual beings? Must mankind only be slaves or captives? Are we not now gods?

SUPRAMUNDANE BEING (infuriated):

-Can humankind transform to godkind? Has cat ever undergone transfiguration into a lion? Has butterfly ever transmuted to a bird? Can lizard evolve into crocodile? Has worm ever changed to snake? Even though the talkative parrot can fly, can it fly high to touch the sky like the silent eagle? Has parrot ever metamorphosed into an eagle? Have you ever seen the shadow of flame (Fire)?

Creatures are kind by kind, so are beings, role by role; stop hoping against hope: you cannot become another kind, a new kind, "born again".

Be content with your role. Every creature plays its role. Play your role, instruments in the hands of spiritual beings, to be taken to blissful or blastful eternity.

ALEXANDA (almost begging):

-Has the time not come for us to be free? From our creation, we have evolved: saved, sanctified, justified, translated, and immortalised. We have learnt the ways of superior beings. We should by now, be like them, free as they are, not tied to the apron-string of other beings. Freedom is our birth-right.

SUPRAMUNDANE BEING (Irritably, like a defeated advocate, to ALEXANDA):

-Your blueprint is conceived in service. Your DNA is sequenced for servility. Servitude is cast in the stone of your nature. Obsequiousness is ingrained in your soul. Slavishness is planted in your spirit. Your gene is encrypted for service. Your functionality is service-specific in code and design: which of these are decryptable or which of these tentacles are "unlockable?"

ROSALINDA (For the first time, enlivened, to ALEXANDA, with a sardonic grin):

-Exactly what you said to me (and to all women). So, is man also a servant, malleable, modifiable, modulated, manipulated, controlled from above, by higher beings, from a higher domain? Punch-bag for spiritual beings. Pounding mortar for superior beings, pelted from above, buffeted from all sides, victimised by all beings, only superior to feminists. Man, the master of women is slave to the gods. Women's dependency on men is a real-world example of human dependency on the spirits.

Man, your superiority is temporary, evanescent, vanity, fake, null, void and of no significance. There is a superseding superiority, enduring, everlasting. All the arrows he fires at feminists are sent back to him by spiritual beings. All that man does to woman, similar measure he receives from the higher beings.

Chief servant enslaving the servant in the community of slaves, made for service in the community of slaves - the tyranny of the gods over Humanity is reflected as the oppression of man against womanity, misplaced aggression. Truly, feminism exemplifies, demonstrates and replicates in the terrestrial realm the conflict and strife between rival powers in the spirit realm.
(Turns to the judgment throne):
-Permit me to relay these findings to my living love-ones, especially, the feminists. Surely, men and the feminists are play-acting the rivalry in the other realm.

AMANDA (muters inaudibly, aside):
-Surely, feminism is the replica of the war (conflict and strife) in the other realm.
(Speaking naively, this time to ROSALINDA, defending her forbidden love. Effortlessly fluent):
-As women need protection from indiscriminate violations from all men so do humans need protection from

attacks by the gods. But he is defending us. He speaks on our behalf, in our interest and seeks our freedom from "independence in dependence". He is a good leader, seeking freedom for his kind from superior spirit-kind. Poor hapless souls, pliant and biddable, created good to be culled, cullable, corrupted to be trashed and threshed, blighted and in a plight that requires remediation, preferred ones to be elected into the silos, rejected ones winnowed into the fire, the selection to be by sifting. Was man consulted before his creation or his Culling, corruption and perfection, election or selection, acceptance and rejection, sieving and winnowing? Were all not at the consensus of the gods, before his beginning? Is it now that he is pliable and biddable, tugged between goodness and wrathfullness, changes and war, and each beast of burden is goaded and doing whatever he is bidden to do that man will exercise his freedom to choose where he will spend eternity?

SUPRAMUNDANE BEING (interjects, forcefully):
-Were you goaded in your thoughts, words, or deeds: when you committed murder, adultery, bore false witness, stole, defrauded others, disobeyed your mother and father?

ALEXANDA:
-You desired him, entered into his heart, hardened his heart and besides, the blood that was shed covered all.

SUPRAMUNDANE BEING:
-Were you bidden with your haughty eyes, hands that shed innocent blood, a lying tongue, a heart that devises wicked schemes, a false witness who pours out lies, feet that are quick to rush into evil?

ALEXANDA:
-The blood, the blood, the blood on the cross...is sufficient atonement.

SUPRAMUNDANE BEING:
-Were you prodded with your lust, gluttony, laziness, greed, wrath, envy and blasphemy against the Holy Spirit?

ALEXANDA:
-The blood purified us from all.

SUPRAMUNDANE BEING:
-So, the blood is your newfangled evidence? The justification for sins? The excuse for derailment? The atonement? Should you continue in your freedom because the blood abounds? Should you continue in your foolishness because Grace abounds?

ALEXANDA:
-It is not his fault, you made him so, desired him, entered into his heart, hardened his heart and controlled him from there – the blood availleth him Mercy – because it is not his fault.

SUPRAMUNDANE BEING:
-Blood flows only in life. Grace abounds only when you are alive. The fish in a dried river knows no Mercy – but certain death. Death seals disobedience and obedience. Death gavels the judgment note. Death is the mallet with which the expiration of Mercy is announced. And you were impenitent at death. You rejected salvation till the end – so the door was closed against you. It is medicine after death.

ALEXANDA (caustically):
-So, my brother who has not tasted death is covered by the blood and will never taste death?

SUPRAMUNDANE BEING:
-Your brother has been condemned by the rebellion of one.

ALEXANDA:
-ALL were condemned automatically by the trespass of one, likewise, by one, were ALL acquitted (justified) unto life by the propitiation for the disobedience of the world and the reconciliation of the world unto himself.

SUPRAMUNDANE BEING (scathingly):
-The actualization of that acquittal is still in his hands to work out before it can manifest. That mere declaratory verdict of acquittal is akin to a mere offer of "flight ticket". Has he obtained the boarding pass or waited patiently at the departure hall for flight departure announcement? Has he embarked on the flight? Where has he landed? Where has the access to the flight ticket landed him? Or put in another way, has he accepted the atonement? Does he conform to the terms of the blood covenant? Does he service the altar of the blood covenant and continue in it? Nothing goes for nothing! Is the redemption by the blood unconditional? Is he without lapses? For if he enjoys the benefits of the blood covenant and then derails, discredits it again – it is better a stone is tied to his neck and he is thrown into the sea, his end is worse that his beginning – for humans must service one altar or the other – the altar of life (blood) or the altar of death. But for you that have tasted death without insurance cover, without accepting the atonement, you are legally entrapped here.

ALEXANDA:
-It is too hot here and there is no water, our throats are dry, we will die of thirst.

SUPRAMUNDANE BEING:
- You will not die here but will live in the heat and groan endlessly from the thirst.

ALEXANDA:
- My wife here should go back and bring us water to wet our throat.

SUPRAMUNDANE BEING:
- Here, there is no wife, there is no marriage, there is no male and there is no female - alone you came and alone you will account for your deeds. All are souls, equal before their maker, accountable for their deeds.

ALEXANDA:
-Then her sister here should go back to warn our kins to mend their ways lest they fail and derail and still end up here. If one went from here, they might repent.

SUPRAMUNDANE BEING:
-Neither will they be persuaded, though one went from here. The prophets are there, the scriptures are there - the Grace over there is sufficient for all; the Thomases and the Judases who were prepared for me will still end up here.

ALEXANDA:
-Because you designed them so, and desired them and hardened their hearts before they were conceived.

SUPRAMUNDANE BEING:

- Yes, because they were destined to be in my penitentiary from the beginning before their condemnation manifests in the physical.

ALEXANDA:

-Were they truly condemned before conception?

SUPRAMUNDANE BEING:

-Condemnation is a process. It is a part of the process of separation just as salvation.

ALEXANDA:

-Why the separation?

SUPRAMUNDANE BEING:

-The weeding of the tares to spare the wheat from choking, the sieving of the grains into the silos for preservation, the winnowing of the chaff into the fire for destruction and the permanent segregation of Evil from Good, the reformed from the deformed for the attainment of peace and the elimination of corruption. Separation of the condemned from the saved for the purpose of asset sharing among the gods. The saved have their destination and the condemned have a separate destination - as is in the will of the gods - the kingdom that suffereth violence must be separated from the kingdom that suffereth not. And separation is in the blueprint of Human-kind project - so evil ones will not corrupt good ones.

ALEXANDA:

-Even with their public penance?

SUPRAMUNDANE BEING:

-Penance of the lips does not purgate the motive of the heart.

ALEXANDA (soberly):

-With this newfound understanding, we are now penitent and will mend our ways and be obedient to our creator.

SUPRAMUNDANE BEING (laughs out loudly, with self-assured hubris):

-Too late in the day, lol, your time is up and the game is over, and the harvest is done and the destination is here - you reap what you sow - you put the blood to shame and crucified the blood a second time to earn a second death. The die is cast. You have crossed the Rubicon to serve the throne of cause and effect, the consequences of your actions and your destiny is in hell.

SUPREME BEING (dourly):

-Today, the 'saved' and the 'lost' will be judged, both good and bad thoughts, words, and deeds of persons who come or refuse to come to me in faith, all will face the laws of cause and effect, the Righteous will go to their eternal reward in heaven and the damned will go to hell. Today, the conclusion of the work of SEPARATION, light will be separated from darkness, impurities from the pure and darkness will not prevail against light - on this final day of perfection.

My rewards, the crowns of being blameless, becoming beacons (bright lights shining out clearly in the world of darkness), bringing the brightness to full effect and maintaining this to the end are with me to be given to those who merit them. Today, the good kingdom will be separated from the bad Kingdoms, while all that are not good will be cast into the well of burning fire, to burn forever; the beacons will be separated from the embers and the cinders will burn to ashes - the beacons, in their mansions as landlords will shine for ever.

SUPRAMUNDANE BEING (with suzerainty):

-We, the gods have worked together this long for this cause, but on this final day of judgment, the day of permanent separation: evil, wickedness, the deformed, the Goats on one side, good, righteousness, the reformed, the Sheep on the other side; today I will take what is mine to my tent, take yours away to your eternal tent, that there may be peace in the bottom of our hearts.

ROSALINDA, AMANDA AND ALEXANDA (together, with audacity):

-The WAR in the spirit realm over the sharing of human asset between the domains of the gods, akin to the war on free expression of thought, is not in human interest. To your Kingdoms, O ye gods! Go your separate ways and leave us, humans, and our Kingdom out of your supremacy conflict. We are not poodles sicked onto by the gods. We are thwarted by your magisterial presence. Enough of the tyranny of the gods - every beginning has an end.

ALEXANDA (defiantly):

-We are not pawns on the chessboard nor football to be kicked about in the pitch of the gods, not in betting markets nor are gambling chips, or dice for dancing and dicing by the gods; not coupons for forecasting nor lots to be cast and shared among the gods. We were created but are now creators of our spheres, created as humans but have evolved into gods, not to be picked by lottery, not goats to be goaded, not sheep to be prodded nor be separated and selected by casting of lot by the gods.

ROSALINDA (with an intransigent attitude):

-Humanity is not a threesome game of the gods, to be ping-ponged from pillar to post, nor are humans baseball

66

to be pilloried by baseball bat. Enough of tossing humans from one god to the other. Every beginning has an end.

AMANDA (obstinately):
-In our own right, we are humans, corporate, creative, independent, of same image and likeness - are beings just like the gods. This final day of perfection should be for the separation of the human kingdom from the kingdom of the gods. The bread is in your hands, the knife is in your hands, we know, but justice demands that you cut with equity, fairness and Mercy not with insouciance or animus towards us. The sovereignty of the gods is without arbitrariness. Through technology the science of knowing the way of the gods and doing what they do, we have evolved into gods just as you are and must be free in our Kingdom as you are in your domains. Humans have been primed all along and are now ripe to be freed. Humans must be free from the control of the spirit-kind.

ALEXANDA:
-As he that is down needs fear no fall, we that are dead need fear no second death. Limited and inevitably bound under spiritual control and subpar in the natural hierarchy of beinghood, sub-ordinate, in submission, of same essence but lower being, humans, need fear no further ounces of magisterial deliberacy of the gods.

SUPRAMUNDANE BEING (with vainglorious sense of triumphalism):
-We were together as a team working for the purpose of separating the reformed from the deformed until I had my own kingdom. In spite of your vast empire you are jealous and interested in mine. Even if you claim the conception of Human-kind project, remember when you said "Let us make man..." Together, we mid-wifed, nursed,

67

trimmed and pruned the project. Now is the harvest time, justice demands that we must reap and share together. Sovereignty negates arbitrariness.

You made Humans, I concede without accepting, I also made so much impact on humanity that I am as much entitled to a portion of Humanity as you are. Today, the final day of this war, in which there is no winner and no loser, the declaration of our treaty of none interference in each other's kingdom, I will take away my entitled portion of Humanity, even if you claim they are condemned or lost, they are the saved to me, they are my gains for all the years of moulding them to my taste. They are my elects, the ones after my heart, the ones I chose before they were conceived - they are not useless, I mentored them to my taste. Lol... they will serve at least as pepersoup in my kingdom. Lol.

THE SUPREME BEING (wrathfully, with finality, thunders):
-I created man to fellowship with me.

I gave the world and all the food in it to him. Instead of thanking me for the woman I also gifted him, not to mention the hidden treasures of darkness in store for him, in place of counting his blessings one by one, man prefers Freedom to the protection that stems from fellowshipping with me. The ungrateful man then has chosen the freedom to perish as he allowed the serpent to outmaneuver and snatch from him the dominion he had on a platter of gold.

I created the serpent for a purpose. Along the line, he developed wings, pride, ambition, ideas, attitude, and imagination when he cannot even translate these to reality - what the almighty creator does at just a command.

As the crooked serpent did not make himself so did humans not create themselves. I the Lord God made them both. But each is bent on his personal agenda, that is nothingness (emptiness, vanity), but will crash into doom. Still bent on freedom, rebellion, deviation, departure, separation and death.

Only in dependence can humans be free when what is against them is not blood and flesh, but changes and war by mysterious hands. Until I put their enemy under their feet, freedom for humans only comes from their trusting their creator wholeheartedly, stretching out their hands to Him, putting away their sins, no evil in their hearts, then they will be free from fear, captivity, death and hell.

You were given a long rope. You had enough time to make your choice. You had your chance. The grace was sufficient for you. Your preachers were many and your prophets were countless, and they did their best. Your saviour was there, the comforter was there. The history was there. You have ears but will not hear, even the testimonies. You have eyes but will not see, even the signs, wonders and miracles. The hardness of your heart will not let you believe your creator. You have understanding but will not know that unless you align with the Supreme Being, the Supramundane being will devour you. You are up against principalities and power. You frittered away every opportunity. You squandered the grace. And you lost the hope, the peace, the rest. You missed everything but doom.

I am your creator, not willing that any should perish but that all should come to repentance; I am long suffering, merciful, forgiving, just. But I will never let a sinner go unpunished.

You rebels, bent on self-destruction! Stiff-necked, with hardened hearts. Appealing, cajoling or preaching to you is like pouring water on a duck's back: of no use. You will not know my Glory. You will not know peace, the peace that passes all understanding. You will not have rest but damnation. You have rejected my type of freedom for your type of freedom.

Perdition you have chosen. Perish you must. (Bangs the gavel so hard and angrily such that the loudest sound ever heard was produced). In fear, like sparks, the trio jumps out of the judgment throne, but lands in the well of burning fire. The accuser, prosecutor-cum- human-tormentor elatedly returns to the well of burning fire that appears to be his eternal home.

Curtain falls.

EPILOGUE OF HUMANITY IN THE HAND OF DIVINITY
AN EPISTLE TO MY PEOPLE

It is my turn, I've earned it. Been travelling the world over to actualize it.

This is one such journeys.

As I sat at the departure hall, clutching my boarding pass, anticipating the voice of the announcer: flight number..6666, my mind wandered out beyond the horizon, wondering, does the pilot know our destination? If he knows our destination and knows our departure time, does he know when we will land? He knows his craft well after years of training and flying but does he know how the flight will be?

Well trained, tested and trusted, but, will he be the only one controlling his craft, landing time and place? I am conscious of the manipulators - invisible, invincible, incorporeal but real and the part they play in the affairs of Humankind.

Everything is in the hands of God including my turn too., but I must play my part - claim and try to actualize my turn.

My young, courageous, brilliant promising lawyer, Efiom Ini, in court today, while defending his client, gesticulated with a demeanour the judge did not like and smiled at the judge the way she did not fancy and so, infuriated, over a clash between insubordination and intemperance, rude and contemptuous behaviour, or the offal of vendetta, the judge, who had in the past threatened to jail him unless he conforms or purgates contempt off his heart, at her whims, ordered him to step out of the bar, and derobe.

He was not asked to enter a dock, no charge was read to him, no opportunity was afforded him to make any plea nor say anything, without trial, she convicted, sentenced and committed him to prison - for one month. He went to court from his house that day only to be taken to the prison. That morning, he kissed his wife and children, then said, see you in the evening before leaving.

They expected him back home that day - but that wasn't the arrangement by the gods for him , but a transition from a lawyer to a prisoner or transpositioning from his home to prison. The prison was his destination - even as a learned man, his destiny is in the hands of the gods - he can sue them after doing their will. The destiny of man is in the hands of his overriding beings.

At a twinkle in my life, I witnessed the transmogrification from the robed advocate to a forcefully shaven "designaturized"[1] cowed prisoner who was hand-cuffed , 'debearded', made to sit on the floor and made a spectacle of - like the transmigration of the soul - all to show the overriding role of the gods, the judge, in the affairs of human existential progression - theirs is to take you to their designated destination. In this case, from a free man to a convict then to ex-convict to prove that they are in charge of human affairs.

Today again, from this newspaper in my fidgety hand, a 36-year-old man, bubbling with good health, high hopes and aspiration, after spending 28 years abroad from age 8, took a flight to his country.

He wanted to take his people by surprise and so informed only his dad.

---

[1] The removal of hairs from the face of a convict to humiliate him and make him unrecognisable.

72

His mother and siblings did not even know he was coming home.

At the airport, his dad saw his airplane land, saw him disembark, but then security agents wisked him away to an unknown destination.

The young inexperienced man, alarmed and unsure of their motive and his destination, attempted to escape, the security agents opened fire and killed him on the spot.

The young man's destination was his country, but the gods had a different destiny for him.

His father expected him home that day, but the gods took him home instead.

That is Destiny - the decision of the supretending beings - was his transition from one being form to another and transpositioning from the land of the living to the land of the dead to demonstrate the overriding role of the gods in the life of human beings.

As old as I am, my hands and legs are shaking, my lips are heavy and sagging, words come out of my mouth with difficulty, my knees after many operations are bent and, in spite of using diapers my clothe still gets wet from dribbling urine, all pointers to my age and health, yet, I must not rest, because it is our turn.

Today I must be in Trinidad after a stopover at Toronto via Chicago to connect Conecticuit, all to actualize our turn. I worked hard for it, it has been my life ambition. I own a tenth of Lagos and so much in Abuja but unless I take over Aso rock I cannot rest. Why should I rest? God has blessed me with property, but I am surrounded by poverty. My people are very poor. So, it is my turn to take over power and distribute property to my people - to take away their poverty - and give them a new destiny, the assignment ceded to me by the gods -

rescuing the poor. My mind reels from this challenging responsibility.

What will my rivals not say about me? Some say I am from Irapin, others say I am from Larpin, still others talk of unascertained genealogy - what are all these to the gods?

From age discrepancies to usurped title, names and phony academic diplomas - when man was made and He breathed into him and man became a living soul - were all these issues? There is only one pedigree - the image and likeness of God.

God put a part of him in man and so the only origin of man is God - what is Larpin, Irapin or genealogy then when we have one and same origin?

My opponents claim that I forfeited humongous amount of dollars in a plea bargain for jail term after drug-related conviction... this humour, in attempt to torpedo my turn... are they my God?

Assuming but not conceding,

Should the beneficiary of plea bargain be punished twice for the same offence? Have old things not passed away? After atonement, am I not a new creature? Am I not born-again?

So did they say bullion-van I worked for contains money. What is bullion-van meant for.? Then they said the money was for election. What is usually used for election - water? Next, they said the election was rigged. Did Trump not say Democrats rigged election because their candidate was old? Today, is that candidate not defeating Russia by proxy? Why is it that when it is my turn, there is harvest of needless questions? Just because I said the greatest election rigger in this country is an expired meat and must be Dumped in the dustbin and be Forgotten about? Yes! Humans do expire - especially when senescence jams sicknesses.

My challengers also say I have many names and suffer memory lapses; what is 'memory lapses' when some before me became vegetables but were still presidents and others transmigrated but are still presidents in spite of that inevitable voice that cannot be disobeyed, they still had their way? Is it because it is my turn?

Even if I do medical tourism, is the world not a global village? In this computer age, can't I rule from any part of the world? Is it because it is my turn?

We dream every day, but not a dot is known about dream.

We sleep every day, but not a dot is known about sleep.

We live every day, but not a lot is known about life.

So, how am I to know about my flight, my turn, my presidency and others I do not taste every day.

All I know is hope to actualize my turn to distribute property in my presidency to poverty-stricken people, for the gods designed the rich and the poor and mandated the rich to deliver the poor from poverty - the rich are the gods of the poor. I also have hope to land safely in this flight - my destiny.

I was not anointed but bulldozed my way through these thousand obstacles by my adversaries to open a thousand doors into my turn because the gods are with me. That was why, when they said I am a senile, decrepit old man, I asked "will I break stones in Aso-rock?[2] Can't I hire bricklayers?" Dissemination of propaganda is electioneering strategy.

---

[2] The seat of government in Abuja, capital of Nigeria.

Try as they may, ultimately, everything is in the hands of the gods. The God who made the camel pass through the eye of a needle and the rich man to enter heaven will see me through into my turn.

It is my turn, to rescue my country by looking into its problems: poverty distribution inequality, Christianisation versus Islamization, Biafranization[3] versus Fulanization[4], Babbling Biafrans versus Bourdillonism.

Blasphemy in expression of thoughts, majority right over minority right, domination versus subjugation, mutual distrust and divisiveness. Pauperization polemics.

There are other problems but the above are made in my country's problems - that it is my turn to solve. My country - the land of impossibilities.

And here I am at the departure hall of my embarkation port, clenching fitfully at my boarding pass, waiting for the expected announcement for flight 6666 to take off. To my contenders, everything about me is uncertain: my age, origin, qualifications, my turn, will I distribute property or poverty in my presidency? Whether I am human or superhuman - some even quipped - he is a political genius with sagacity, a master-tactician, a strategist - the disputation, the uncertainties continue.

To me, what are uncertain are my flight and where I will land. The only important things are: will the flight be turbulence and crash free? And, when eventually the final flight lands, will I land on the bosom of Abraham, comforted, with drips of water into my throat to cool my tongue and quench my thirst? Or will I land where the gulf will separate me from Father Abraham and be

---

[3] The creation of a dot in a circle, as Biafra nation out of Nigeria
[4] The domination of Nigeria by the Fulani.

scorched by heat and tormented in flame? What is the will of the gods concerning these?

To my people, what concerns them is my turn, my presidency and distribution of poverty or property. To me everything concerning humanity is in the hands of the gods: my presidency, this flight and my landing and even my final flight ✈.

To my people, presidency means distribution of poverty or property, to me, my turn means where will I land - my destiny. All I have is hope to console myself.

But what is paramount is my landing place. Just as the doctor cares but God heals, so do humans try but the gods decide... Man proposes, God disposes.

Choose between one and the other! What is in choosing what you did not plan, design, propose nor have control over? Can I even control my choice? Nope! All I can do is wish I can.

My allies say all I have to do is choose where I will land. Who will not choose to land on the bosom of Father Abraham? When it is in the hands of the gods, they decide what they want - they share the landing pad and share the passengers among themselves because they are the gods. What are humans to them but passengers to be shared to the landing ports - then shared among the gods. The effort is for me to make, the Crown is in the hands of God to Crown whoever he chooses.

This is what eternity is all about - sharing of passengers among the gods - human schism - sorting out: tares from the wheat, chaff from the grain, good from evil, then shared between other gods and the Highest.

This is what human life is all about - passage of Humans into the hands of the gods - the overseeing beings. So, what should the passengers do to be shared to land unto Abraham's bosom except to be at the mercy of their whims?

My people, for you, to take my turn is a must, my co-passengers, in this flight, to land safely is our wish, for me, in my final flight ✈, to land on Abraham's bosom is the goal - the plan and the thoughts of the Almighty towards me.

So, my people, shoot your choice wisely to land in comfort. Or choose your poison las las to land in torment. So, when I say it is my turn, I mean my turn to land. The effort is mine to make, the reward is God's to give. As I behold, not through the figment of my imagination,

The scouting hawk, from its hunt swoop on the wandering chick, the prowling lion, from its ambushment, pounce on the straying gazelle, the bald eagle, from its vanguard, dive onto loon chicks, the coiled python, from its wait, project to coil round and constrict its prey, the convinced judge, in her verdict, sentence the convict to prison terms, the threatening cloud, from her overriding position, entombed the wide Earth, and, the Almighty God, in his majesty, decide the Fate of Humankind,

Do I see the futility of furious feminism, the fruitlessness of rebellious arrogance, and understand the beauty of the submission of the wife to her husband, and the need for Humanity to yield to Divinity, as it now dawns on me that all has been prearranged to show that the Fate of Humankind is in the hands of the spirit-kind, and I appreciate the helplessness of humanity concerning his own Destiny.

That's how I received the news that the Sun will die out in eleven billion years, as my hands cannot even touch the sky. Moreover, a pawn in the hands of the gods, what will I do for eleven billion years?

And the Sun, the Moon, Humanity, all are in the hands of Divinity, who on the dot substituted Condemnation with Salvation.

Who then am I to know the outcome of my FLIGHT, nor determine the outcome of the quest for MY TURN. Nor can I determine my final disembarkment port. So, all I have to do is: accept whatever I cannot change.

That was how my young courageous lawyer walked from his house to the court from whence he was moved to the prison - without option of choice. My abroad returnee flew to his country from whence he was translated to the great beyond - he had no choice too.

And so, as I pursue my turn and as I board this flight ✈, I know that my destination is not in my hands, nor is my disembarkation point. And, in my final flight ✈, my resting place is not at my command.

To all, there is a choice that lands one in comfort and there is a choice that lands one in torture and above all: only the Highest can give us our turn. And grant us gòod rest - all other gods can only offer torment.

If I win, I will rule with the fear of God, for if my ways please Him, then will He land me on the bosom of Abraham.

HUMANS SHALL BE FREE
CAST:

ROSE
PASSERS-BY 1, 2, 3
CYCLIST
TRADER
RHAHAAB
LANRE
LANRE 'S FATHER
LADY
MAMA IBE
CHIEF IBECHUKWU
ALICE AND BEKI

ACT ONE. SCENE ONE

Beauty empowers and opens doors for you, but it does not guarantee a beautiful life nor happiness, nay marriage and it also imperils you.
It is merely a tool used by the gods to lead or mislead humans to the place prepared for them.

Year 2021 A.D. A street. An evening. A tranquil country place.
Everyone is mindful only of their business.
Suddenly, Rose sweeps majestically round a bend in the street and, like the moon over the horizon, emerges in her most genteel manner.
She wears a natural beauty accentuated by artificial make-ups with exquisite fragility, agility, the fragrance of a flower, fascinating innocence reminiscent of a sleeping baby, and is at the apogee and most rewarding phase of femininity.
She is tall, fair-complexioned, beautifully and fashionably dressed, highly cultured and her mannerism has a delicate charm and a touch of pride.
Rose is an epitome of the conflict between the conservatism of nature and the influences of all the schools of modernity.
She moves with the freedom and flexibility of a spineless creature with each calculated graceful step setting up ripples after ripples of wrinkles round her neck, with deep-seated eyes radiating joy, contentment, confidence and roving invitingly.
The nimbleness with which she appears in the street stops every action. Everyone is held spellbound and breathless; all attention is focused on her.

(*Rose on her way home, noticing that all eyes are on her, overhears some passers- by*)

FIRST PASSER–BY (His eyes dilating, impulsively, to his colleagues, points to Rose as she sails away from them with studied elegance and dignity):
-This is the height of Supernal architectural feat: a petite sylph-like nymph.

SECOND PASSER-BY (murmuring inarticulately, lustfully):
-The sight of her sets all hearts throbbing, all pulses pausing, all eyes converging, with this ethereal beauty as the convergent point.
Her steps of feline grace, her velvety skin, her perfect curves; this sight for sore eyes is a feast for the gods.

(*Rose moves on with practised queenly carriage*)

THIRD PASSER-BY (leering at Rose with surging enthusiasm, adds, unctuously):
-This ineffable beauty can ne'er surfeit the optic stars. I wear my heart on my sleeves for her.

(*Suddenly, a cyclist carrying a woman with a baby on her back and a basin of garri on her head, while ogling Rose, rides into a group of women hawking articles on the pavement. The bicycle falls on the traders, scattering all their wares*)

TRADER (laughing and jesting by everybody at the scene. All the women curse, abuse and beat the cyclist):
-Ninny, haven't you seen a young girl before?

CYCLIST (as he tries to get up, petulantly):
-This one is different from all the girls I've seen before. There is no river nearby, I would have mistaken her for a 'Mma-mi-water.' If I'm able to have her - as my last earthly accomplishment, or even as my last super - I will be fulfilled.

FIRST PASSER-BY (with arms folded across his chest; shocked, phlegmatically):
-Providence, thou art king of partiality; whereas countless damsels Roam about in search of men, who will do as much as say "hello" to them, here is a good sort, this pearl amongst women, endowed to the fullest measure with beauty which makes men scramble for her even at the cost of their lives.

SECOND PASSER- BY (prosaically):
- On seeing her, men lose their senses. Even the proud, the pompous, become beggarly. It happens every day, these my eyes are the witnesses, like yesterday, whilst she was on her way home, in front of my abode, a beetle-car driver parked by her:
'Eh! Babe, mind a lift?' - wooed the proud car owner, expectantly.
With a last disdainful look, her head cocked, sardonically, she rejected emphatically.
'I don't accept lifts in boxes'
The car driver, whose sex was cowed and goaded by humiliation, sped off unhappily.
Hardly was he gone than an old, panelled Benz-car stopped by her.
'Hi beauty, care for a lift?' - offered the car owner eagerly.
With a withering scornful look, she spurned him outrightly.

85

'I don't accept lifts in old "cargoes"'.

'The body is old, but the engine is strong' - argued the persistent helper, disarmingly.

As vain as a peacock, she shouted off her nuisance: 'No! No!! No! Not for me. Strong wine in old wine skin is not for me' - she emphasized, superciliously.

THIRD PASSER-BY (cynically):

-That was casting pearls before the swine. Maybe she does not accept lifts 'cause it's synonymous with prostitution.

SECOND PASSSER-BY: (ecstatically):

-Whilst we watched with mouth agape, as she walked off with lissomness, shortly a wee bit distance away, a brand-new baby-benz-car screeched to a halt just by her. 'Baby bird, a ride home?' - suggested the rich man, anticipitatorily, with soft feline politeness.

To our greatest surprise, with dignified entitlement, she purred her approval with an imperial gesture. Like Elizabeth Reginal, she held out her hand imperiously, even aided to enter the dazzling car with an imperious manner.

While we were still held spellbound and frozen with surprise by this feast for the eyes and balm for the soul, the rich man car owner, grinning with satisfaction, carted his conquest away, the way the king lion captures and gloats over its prey.

FIRST PASSER-BY (Profoundly):

-Perks of being a rich man include "Bush meat allowance, point and take away", being beneficiary of the freshest ripe fruit from the tree, and awardee of the right of best choice.

I must make money in this life. I must be rich at all costs, so that I will earn the best babes the world can provide.

SECOND PASSER-BY (Sensationally):
-She deserves the title she won: Miss World, from the world's most beautiful girl contest. That is a general acceptance and a public endorsement as the beauty of beauties.

THIRD PASSER-BY (wearing a blank flabbergasted expression, with mind blown, and mouth opened):
-As the trophy is for the swiftest, and Survival is for the fittest, and Supremacy is for the strongest, and the throne is for the heir, so is a beautiful woman for the highest bidder and women the bounties of riches.

But beauty itself is the bounty of nature, and women are graced with this bounty of God only to be pruned down to bounties for rich men -as point and kill or takeaway, endowed with succulence only to be conditioned to hanging their legs on bed for the GRINDER - this is the paradox of womanity or the punishment for feminism, Just as HIV is the recompence of promiscuity or infidelity.

For it is axiomatic that the selfsame source of bounteous beauty of women, divine providence of nature also auctioned women to the highest bidder - the prerogative of Divinity - to elevate and to subdue, the Fate of Humankind is to be cosseted and corseted by the spirit-kind, hence the spirit-kind is bi-faceted to coddle and to crush.

(*Everyone looks on distantly, over where Rose disappeared to, deeply mummified*)

FOURTH PASSER-BY (initially dazed, then regaining his composure, breaks his silence):

- Ripe fruits are coveted by many, so are men entranced by endowed women and so do well-endowed women attract admirers, some will poke the bear.

Good-looking women are enticing, cannot escape toasting and will not lack wooers, because they are ripe and have been primed for men to feast on, even rangers cannot deter the poachers.

Attractive women are like hot cake that sells quickly, like a good ride that will never lack riders, and like a tasty snack that will seldom remain unsold. Though not as scarce as hen's teeth, were they to be in abundance will still not surfeit men's appetite. And, unlike farmland, a beautiful woman can never lie fallow.

Like a precious stone, a succulent woman cannot escape notice.

As beacons shine out clearly in darkness and darkness comprehends it not, even lampshades cannot bring back the darkness, so do captivating women dazzle men's eyes into enchantment - dulling their senses - even the gate of reason cannot prevail.

And, in an alluring woman, Coyness is only an invitation.

Beautiful women are not like 'leftovers' that rats can stumble on and dig into but like valuable condiments, too precious to be within the reach of church rats.

As food that is flavoured, spiced and packaged increases hunger, so does a woman adorned with good clothe and anointed with Beauty arouse anticipation by men.

Crude oil fetches foreign exchange earnings and simultaneously damages the environment, Fuel provides energy but at the same time poisons the climate - causing climate change. So does Beauty advertise the wearer only to take her to the slaughterer.

Beauty is a blessing vouchsafed to women by heaven just to be the cynosure of all eyes but not excluding the eyes of the adversary, the chief Philocalist, waiting on the wings to deliver the same, unfortunately, as bounties to rich men and as sequelae, afflict and infect them with abortion and HIV, making beauty a blessed curse poisoned by communion.

So, granted to the unwary fickle mind, beauty is like a sharp knife in the hands of a little child - that can be used for self-destruction.

The influences of class, position and money on beautiful women are like that of poachers on the forest.

So, be wary, lest beauty that makes you a spectacle to behold becomes your passport to self-destruction: the double-edged sword by which men are entranced, enchanted, and enthralled, should also capture you as the consort of infertility (diseases) or ensnare you into single parenthood or entrap you in life-long spinsterhood or enthrone you in singlehood - the weapon fashioned against humans by the challenger of all that is good.

For as the race is not for the swiftest nor wealth for the wisest so does Beauty not guarantee happiness nor beautiful life, nay marriage but everything happens as has been preset - the work of one and the self-same spirit apportioning individually as He wills for his purpose.

Curtain falls.

ACT ONE. SCENE TWO

Make hay while the sun shines: marry when you are still attractive.

IN THE SITTING ROOM.
Same evening. Same tranquil environment, but the atmosphere is now rather dusky, calm and cool. Rahaab, roughly in her thirties, tall, beautiful, used to be brash, cheeky, cocky but now mellowed by disappointments, experience and maturity, appears on the veranda, takes two dignified steps forward and stands by the door with the inside of the room screened from her view. She is dressed in the latest fashion. Her beauty is accentuated by make-up which masks her earliest crops of wrinkles but fails in her primary intention, that of making her look younger. Her natural paleness is made artificial by excessive and conspicuous make-up and showy dressing together with her wistfully moving eyes, tired looks, fully developed busts and feminine curves and an air of importance, experience and confidence about her. These betray her age and tells the world that she is a full-blown woman- a thing she wishes is not yet so. She epitomizes the overwhelming influences of foreign culture and modernization.
We can see the dimly lit, luxuriously furnished and quiet room through the lace drawn across the window. Rose, who has been lounging on a Swiss-sized sofa, on noticing the approach of a visitor, furtively enters an inner room. Shortly, she stealthily makes her way to the window and spies the visitor.
Rahaab knocks the door over ten times. No reply is forthcoming. She searches for signs of life in the compound with no success. In anger she turns back to go.

ROSE (Peeping through the window repeatedly. Convinced, she gently eases the door, opens):
-My apologies for keeping you waiting outside. Good day and welcome, my auntie.

RAHAAB (Still nettled by her cold reception, turns back and enters the house. She nestles down in a chair, cheekily):
-Where is my friend, your elder sister?

(*Jazz music is faintly heard from the adjoining room*)
ROSE (gaily):

-That hoary haired money-monger has 'towed' her away. Overnight, she told me.

RAHAAB (flaming):
-Is that why you locked the door and wouldn't open to visitors? Or are you inside with a man?

ROSE (Sitting down opposite her, good-humouredly):
-No, 'aunty'. I locked the door because of the ravening wolves. They are a real nuisance. They feel entitled to feast on every damsel. I came back a short while ago.
In that interval, ten of them came knocking. All I do is peep through the window. Once convinced that the intruder is a man, I leave them to their hobby: knocking till their knuckles become sore.
That is the price they pay for being a thorn in my flesh. I mistook you for one of those nuisances when you knocked.

RAHAAB (Pouting, amused, with a cheeky grin):
-Sweet sixteen, (excitedly) this is your turn, so were our lives, in our teens, seethed with lustre they come preying.
This sweet yam must they all taste.

(*Down cast*)

But peri-thirty, when wizened wrinkles suffuse the over caressed genteel curves, locked in limbo, we go begging. Hither and thither they go skulking.

(*Brief pause*)

My dear young one, times have changed. Precious stones no longer glitter because everywhere is now glassy, glossy and flashy. So, strike now while the iron is still hot.

(*Gets up to go*)

Anyway, tell my good friend that I went to Lanre's place but met his absence, so I dropped in here to say hello.

ROSE:
-'Aunty', which Lanre is that?

RHAHAAB (brashly):
-My boyfriend.

ROSE (showing interest, beckons on her to sit down):
-The one you came here with last weekend?

RHAHAAB:
-No, he is my newest boy- friend.

93

ROSE (with callowness, inquisitively):
-'Aunty', why is it that you and my sister always have many boyfriends at the same time? Is one not enough to satisfy a woman's appetite and needs at a time?

RAHAAB (sitting again, then with perfect poetic command):
-That is reminiscent of the tale of the swine in the mire. While the piggies were wallowing in the mud, mother–pig busied herself scooping out the mash from the marsh.
Why do you wallow in poking your snout in the quag-mire?

(*Asked a piggy in the whirling vortex of their rootling*)

Grow up my young one. When you are at my age (ges-ticulating) you'll know why I'm always scratching among the swamp bushes

(*Answered the sow*)

But if I may answer your question: experience! The best teacher asserts that multiple courtship is the surest tailor of the wedding gown. Like tentacles, we've learnt to grasp as many of them as octopus can suck so that if nine fail, the tenth will answer the wedding bell to take the tired spinster to the altar to sing the nuptial pledge: for better for good till money make us part. So, if I must share the search-secret with you, multiple courtship is the only insurance for wearing the wedding gown.

(*Her cell phone rings, she picks it up, but doesn't hear anything. Then the line cuts, she drops the phone angrily, complaining of a country where nothing works*)

I met Lanre for the first time a month ago. Today, I went to tell him the result: I've missed my flower.

ROSE (curiously):
-You did not see your 'monthly visitor? '
-But 'aunty', that is rash. Will he accept responsibility for it just like that, after such a brief encounter?

RHAHAAB (off handedly):
-Did you say brief encounter? Even from a one-night, one-touch stand, he cannot shirk his responsibilities.

ROSE:
-Why the rush? Why the desperation?

RHAHAAB:
-Needs must, they say, when the devil drives. At thirty-five, an "emeritus" spinster, what else do I do?
From philtre to donating generously, donating freely; from the mellow yam at long weekends to valentine's gifts, even sailing close to the wind: which one have I not tried?
Believing erroneously that the best way to a spouseless man's heart is by satisfying all his needs. Not knowing that our abundant but elusive bachelors have blocked the portal of their hearts to all nuptial impulses.

(*Sits down*)

How many of them have I not set my cap at? Lanre is my twelfth catch this year: a capital 'no' they have all chorused to all my marriage insinuations.
Since chronic bachelors have developed deaf ears to nuptial solemn toll, perfected evasion of the altar without batting an eyelid, we have also learnt how to force the horse to the river, mindless of its supping there from.

A hard nut to crack like dearth of husbands deserves deeds of derring–do as solution.

ROSE (naively):
-But he is your mister, right?

RHAHAAB (poetically):
- Waiting for mister Right is like waiting for the moon, falling from her cosy sin–free domain to this vicious earth.
Wishes are not horses, so beggars won't be horsemen. Stranded at the bus-stop, endlessly waiting to choose my ride, till now that my back is against the wall, can I still be choosy?
More so, knowing fully well that, time is zooming past, The earth is spinning on, the clock is ticking away, my patience is draining fast, strength is fast failing me, my wrinkles are fast cropping up, my beauty is fast fading away, my egg reserve is fast depleting, menopause's official hour is about on the dot.
My mind is made up: to shoot my shot- as a quarter bread is better than none, and welcome is better than bye-bye, and well done is better than sorry, and time waits for no one, all I want is a man, Mister Right or Wrong.
A man I can hold onto, who can hurl upon me the coveted tittle "Mrs", so that I may escape the sneering smiles of job's comforters.

ROSE:
-Has he proposed to marry you?

RHAHAAB:
-Things have changed. Nowadays, "birds fly without perching" because bird- hunters shoot without aiming; so do women make advances at, give green- light to and

propose marriage to men since men avoid marriage like plague. And, since men now see women as burden, budgetable item, women pay to be harboured by men on whose shoulders women's cares are cast.

ROSE:
-Even when there is no love between you?

RHAHAAB:
-The foundation of marriage includes: knowledge, the cares of constant contact, communication and commitment, not love.

ROSE (inquisitively):
-But if you force him to marry you when there's no true love between you, will there be conjugal happiness?

RHAHAAB (matter of factly):
Since love died and resurrected as commitment, our elusive expectation, my young one, Times have changed. In this yahoo dispensation, the hunter no longer gets a thrill out of ambuscades, but scouts for games. So must women not wait to be wooed but shoot their shot. Not just ambushment, women fight to get married, and to keep marriage.

And, also, women no longer wait to be showered with love but shop for love. And shop for attention. And shop for the protection that marriage thrusts upon wives. Women no longer pine for love, they scout for and pay for love.

As a well will not harbour tadpoles the day it is dug, so will love not fall in lines until his cup is full. And, as you must invest before you reap interest, so must he do enough top up before love can germinate. Love is like investment, you only reap when you sow. Respect is reciprocal, so is love. You love first, then expect to be loved.

Love is in the air, like perfume, it can be inhaled and exhaled, respired.

And, love, like disease is communicable. It can be contracted and disseminated.

Love is like vaccine, it can be inoculated. By our gestures, we inject others with love.

The harmony of its calligraphy is in our smiles. By the dissonance or concordance of our deeds love is birthed or buried. Love is transmissible - as I warm myself into the ventricle of his heart so will I infect him with love.

Love is contagious:

with constant contact, seamless integration and insemination love will germinate and grow. Speaking in tongues in the other room fetches marriage faster than love. In fact, what Love cannot do - like carrying a woman to her husband's house, the cares of constant contact or commitment does. Love is old school. What is in vogue is to be bonded and blinded by commitment. I am committed to the cause of marriage, and, like love, I am blind to reason. Love is blind and is not a requisite for marriage. Love is no more - Eve traded love for apple. The serpent absconded with love until Christ came to cultivate love again. Until the rapture, love will not be harvested. Till then, love is experimental.

Besides:

-It is better to be married but unhappily so than to be both unmarried and unhappy. As there're no roses without thorns, so is there no wedlock without a knot. You won't know that you are married unless people tell you so.

Whereas they won't know that you're unhappy unless you tell them so.

(Rose, schooled, sober, sees her off to the door as Rha-haab gets up to go)

My dear, when love is rough with you, you must also be rough with love. Roughness begets toughness. If someone bites your nose mindless of catarrh, will you mind faeces when you bite his anus? Marriage is not for all women, they say. But I say: I must marry, by "fire or by force" (one way or another). I must get my own man, who will at least serve me the odious task of having to zip up my own blouse myself. There are certain things one cannot do for oneself: can the dead bathe themselves? Can the dead bury themselves? A woman needs a man. I must get my own husband.
Bye bye.

(Rose sees her off to the door)

(Rhahaab exits)

ROSE (Touched, soliloquizes as she paces up and down):
-The words of elders are the dictates of experience. Experience: the only degree obtained outside the hedge of academy.

Hay must I make now that the sun is shining; before the sun sets on me, I must obtain the pledge of the man of my dream.

With the tide must I swim. Even though they say men are for all women, but husbands are not for all women or marriage is not for all women, come what may, I must marry. I must get my own man, who will warm up my own soul, kindle my feelings, feed my desires and supply my needs. The search begins.

Curtain falls

ACT ONE. SCENE THREE

Men, men everywhere, not a husband to marry.

THE SITTING ROOM IN LANRE'S HOUSE
A moderately furnished apartment with modern-day setting. Lanre is sitting down on a couch, using his remote controller to turn on the TV set, selecting his station of choice

(A quick-witted buxom beauty enters. She is friendly but reserved)

LANRE (excitedly):
-What a beautiful bag you have in hand! Where are you coming from?

LADY (happily):
-I went shopping for your coming birthday.

LANRE (looking intently into her eyes):
-That was thoughtful of you. What did you buy?

LADY (with a whimsical sense of humour):
-I bought you the latest fashion in town, the black three-piece suit.

(Pulls them out of her bag and hands them over to him, one after the other)

That's the jacket, that's the waistcoat and your pair of trousers.

LANRE (collects them, examines and admires them, flings the waistcoat and jacket over his left shoulder and the trousers over his right one):

-You are the most caring woman on earth. Givers never lack. I can always trust your choice of colour.

LADY (with a radiant demure sexy stance):
-I chose that colour to match my Christmas coat and skirt.

LANRE (warmly):
-A million thanks for your cares.

LADY (reverently):
-I also bought frozen chicken to prepare your favourite food: fried rice.

LANRE (masterfully):
-You are a darling. A woman who cares about a man's stomach cares about his life.

LADY (submissively, beaming with satisfaction):
-I came to clean, wash, iron and cook for you - my duties as your girlfriend. In a moment, I'll be out of the kitchen.
And your favourite dish will be ready.
(Retires to the kitchen.)

(*Lanre returns to the television, continues to press some buttons. Rhahaab arrives, meets the door ajar, gives a single knock, enters and meets Lanre by the television set changing some stations*)

RHAHAAB (dressed in the height of fashion, seductively):
-Hi! Darling Lanre, how are you?

LANRE (sedately):
-I'm fine. And you?

RHAHAAB (blushing):
-I'm fit as a fiddle, dear darling, my lord. Happy birthday in advance.

LANRE (as if hiding something):
-Thank you.

RHAHAAB (smiling winningly):
-I came to wash, iron, feed you and do exercises for you, my wifely duties to my man.

LANRE (reluctantly):
-You are welcome.

ROSE (warmly):
-I also bought presents for your tomorrow's birthday.

LANRE (getting up from his squatting position, skirting the gesture)
-That's very nice of you. Your duties are at my pleasure.

RHAHAAB (with an air of familiarity and possessiveness, smiling winningly):
(Brings things out of her handbag)
-Here is a pair of Italian shoes and a golden wristwatch for you – still my supplementary uxorial duties.

LANRE (fidgety, receives the gifts):
-Thanks.

(Attracted by the intrusion, Lady comes out from the kitchen, with a small pot in her left hand and a wet soapy black iron sponge in the other, continuing the wifely act of washing the pot, unperturbably)

(*Lanre is visibly shaken. Rhahaab looks daggers at the lady, then shifts her gaze to Lanre*)

RHAHAAB (menacingly, with searching scorn):
-Lanre, my heartthrob, who is this? (With jealousy. Pointing to the lady)

LANRE (stammers):
-Rhaa.

RHAHAAB (looks daggers at her, paces to and fro, silence, undecidedly, then breaks the silence, furious, turning to the lady, cheekily):
-Why are you here?

LADY (gives her a long, strange stare, as if trying to understand who she is. Then, walks up to stand nose to nose with Rhahaab, displaying sardonic enjoyment of her rival's discomfiture. In the process, inadvertently stains Rhahaab's clothe with dirt from the pot she came out of the kitchen with. She challenges her, brashly):
-Why are you mooning around here like some love-struck lunatic?

(*An uncomfortable silence follows. The atmosphere is charged*)

RHAHAAB (turns to LANRE, sermonizing):
-So Lanre, my veritable Casanova boyfriend, when you finish sampling tall and fair ladies, you turn to short and dark-skinned ones for your toying pleasure? Sampler of women, you are richly blessed. Ride on and clap for yourself. It is not your fault; destiny has assigned you the sampling role.

(*Lanre gives no reply but the Lady snarls at her*)

LADY (aggressively and in quick succession):
-Bini people will have asked you: "Na only you them born am for?" What they mean is: "Did they give birth to him only for you?" Are you the only cock to crow? Selfish thing! Is there anything a tall person can do that a short person cannot do? Does he use a ladder to climb you? As tall as you are, don't you stoop low for him? Idiotic sex slave.

(She says these with a unique brand of droll self-mockery demonstrating each sentence with her fingers)

RHAHAAB (adjusting her dress, snapping her nose off):
-Husband snatcher, what are you doing here?

LADY (dramatizes her steps and actions):
-Husband thief, who is your husband?

(Rhahaab and lady fight. Four or five neighbours arrive, alarmed by the altercation between the fighters, but they keep a respectful distance)

LADY (shouting):
-She has bitten me, oh!

(She scratches Rhahaab's face with her long nails; both fighters shout and start to bleed)

(Lanre, on seeing the blood, runs out of the parlour. Rhahaab and lady wail, exchange blows)

(The noise brings Lanre's mother and father to Lanre's flat)

LANRE'S FATHER (placatingly):
(Walks towards the fighting ladies)
-Ladies! peace! What is in a man That is worth dying for? When two fight, a third party throws in the olive branch.
Cats and dogs can delight to bark, bite and scratch each other's eyes out, they say, for such is the nature of beasts. But ladies! You must never let gusty anger make you gouge out each other's eyes.

Our babes and sucklings must never learn such angry passions from you would-be mothers. If you cannot share him, bury the hatchet.

There's as good fish in the sea as ever comes out of it. Hold your peace (separates the irate fighters).

(*Lady, with sobs, wipes the blood off her face, deeply wounded. Gets up, pants about tragically*)

(*Exits*)

Rhahaab, as sulky as a bear, wipes blood off her face, still panting, unspeakably jolted, feeling highly humiliated.

(*Exits*)

(*Lanre returns to the room, can't help but feels a tinge of schadenfreude when his mother eyes him squintily*)

LANRE'S MOTHER (Exhilarated, hailing, dancing around and clapping for her son, draws out the words, sarcastically):
-The son of a Lion, toast of spinters, sought-after gem, talk of the town, headache of the bachelorette, deflower or defile or devour whoever, like a sacrificial lamb, presents herself to you, slaughter those who genuflect their opened legs on your altar, climb any mountain that visits

you, and collect whatever goodies they offer you - insurance covers you.

My son, females are created, fashioned with breasts, bathed, blood washed off them, rubbed with expensive fragrant oils, clothed with embroidered fine linen of silk, decked with jewellery of necklace and bracelet for the wrists, adorned with golden rings for the ears, nose and ankle, nurtured with honey, anointed with lovely crown for the head, turned into beautiful queens that are men's for the asking, mere men's pleaser, fit for men's pleasure, suitable for their sweet savour, solely serving their satisfaction, and ultimately to be devoured by them.

The festival fowl or goat is bought, brought home, fed and played with by household members till the D-day that it is slaughtered, roasted and sacrificed for the gods; so are women brought home, fed, and pampered till they are sacrificed for the satisfaction of men. The tradition as prearranged is that meat is sacrificed to the gods. So are women adorned, flavoured, spiced and sacrificed at the altar of men.

Women are 'jara' (extra) for men as humans are for the gods - minced meat! Sacrificial items are displayed at road junctions for the sweet-smelling savour of the gods, so are women adorned and sacrificed at the altar of the ego of men.

Freebies are your right, the right of elusiveness, the right of eligibility.

Turn by turn, now is your time, a paradigm, a demonstration, as prearranged, that as the two kingdoms of the spirit-kind out-smart each other over human souls, so will women compete for men, an instantiation - a spiritual war represented by physical struggle to get a husband. The season of bachelorhood brings perks of bachelordom; savour it wisely, in a circumspect manner, be sneaky, subtle, crafty as you gloat over your conquest, be shrewd but harmless; be lovey-dovey and serpentine as the occasion calls.

(The uninvited neighbours, murmuring among themselves, one after the other, disperse in disgust)

LANRE'S FATHER (Silently stares at his son, with knotted brow, shouts, open mouthed):
-I have told you times without number to marry so that I may have peace of mind. I do not want to carry corpses in this house.
My plangent wisps of marriage insinuations to your ears are like water off a duck's back. I have given you a house. You earn an attractive salary. What is stopping you from marrying after your thirty–sixth birthday?

LANRE (pauses, hesitates):
-Daddy, how much do I have? I still need some one-million-naira marriage loan.

LANRE'S FATHER (after a brief pause):
-One-million-naira marriage loan? Are you going to marry an angel? Isn't it the modern craze for Lavish wedding today and expensive divorce suit tomorrow?

LANRE (imperturbably):
-Daddy, you know my friend had a one-month honeymoon in Mexico.

LANRE'S FATHER (laughing up his sleeve):
-So, you are going to have a one year 'sugar- moon' in Mozambique? Well! When someone needs something, they pay for it. I need peace of mind.
So, I'll pay for it, I'll pay for your wedding and honeymoon. When is the wedding?

LANRE:
-In five years' time.

LANRE'S FATHER (laughs hysterically. Walks to him, cleans dust off his head and shoulders, as if advising him):
-Five years' time? After your fortieth birthday? After you would have excavated and ruined all the young women, and dragged my feet out into the open? Why, my son, are you shirking marriage?

LANRE:
-I've not yet found a woman.

LANRE'S FATHER:
-Not yet found a woman among all the sorts that have been entertaining you?

LANRE:
-The world is a haven of a chaotic assortment of women, just as are colours. The variation of women in configuration, stature, size and status is adaptation for their roles: entertainment, companionship, esteem boosting, baby bearing or serving as Concubines or mistresses - comfort dispensers - the creator of these roles made them all - role-specific. The range allows users to spec their needs. Role on spec.

LANRE'S FATHER:
-So, those ones cannot also double as wives? The only new part in a woman is her clothe - save the colour of their clothe, all women are the same: breast, mouth, mount and womb.

LANRE:

-There is a parallel between the naunces of womanity and dignity, respect, purpose or power - not her clothe or the colour she chooses.

No dad, there are different kinds of women: prostitutes, mistresses, Concubines, baby bearers, comfort-givers and wives. Every woman specs into her purpose. The blueprint determines the potential. The constitution imposes the character, just as the genotype determines the phenotype, so does the encryption dictate the decryption - the gene in the DNA, as set in place by the programmer made it so. Role differential transmigration is only made possible by reversible learning and adaptation. Those who were encrypted as prostitutes turn out as prostitutes, those raw encrypts of wives end as wives, the whole spectrum of womanhood is decryptable that way. "If it is not PANADOL it cannot be like panadol", they say, because, the wife is the soul-mate, the specific missing-rib - the complement for the completeness of her man.

LANRE'S FATHER:

-So, how will you recognise your lost rib? How will you know the wife-material - it's not written on their foreforehead. They have no identification number.

LANRE:

-By toasting all and testing all and tasting many plus scanning a few - differentiation only comes by experiencing some, and, discerning the harmony in their flavours only by savouring the mixture in the pudding.

LANRE'S FATHER:

-Panadol, paracetamol, para... they all cure headache. Cure your headache, pick a woman - all women are the same, potential wives.

LANRE (stiffly):
-I've not found a wife-material yet. I've been looking for a wifely girl all these years.

LANRE'S FATHER (recoils. Voice rises)
-Not yet found a woman, among the whole lot, that is like the sands of the seashore in multitude: uncountable, ubiquitous, at your command, touch and take away or "Point and kill"?

LANRE (poetically):
-It's easy to find a woman but difficult to find a wife.
The ladies you see everywhere are like the waters of the ocean: easy to come by, but too salty to the taste.

LANRE'S FATHER (controlling himself, with the very perfect poetic ability):
-My father married for me (as he walks away from him) when I was a stripling, before I could realize my manhood.
Since you are as adamantine as a mule, I'll give you enough rope. If it takes you a century to find a girl that is like sugar on the tongue, that is your choice, since this oft-told tale is familiar to your ears, that save the colours of their clothe, all women are the same: sour to the gustation.
Married men only manage the vinegar on their tongues and pretend that they're sweet to the taste.

(*Exits*)

Curtain falls.

ACT ONE. SCENE FOUR

The tongue does not always say what the heart says.

A SCENE IN LADY'S ROOM

LADY (the atmosphere is cheerless. The apartment is in a secluded area. In shorts, lolling on a sofa, to Lanre, who just entered. Nonchalantly):
-I thought your feet will never kiss my abode again, after you asked your girlfriend to kill me in your house. See the wound with which she smirched my spotless face as price for my unrequited love for you. That's what life is: for some, to love is to err, a big sin in some quarters.

LANRE (Leaves his seat, sits near her, pleadingly):
-She is not my girlfriend.

LADY (shifting away from him, cynically):
-But you invited her to your house at the same hour that I honoured a similar invitation.

LANRE (defensively, and grinning armourously at her):
-I did not invite her.

LADY (looking at him, unbelievingly):
-The great cupid, the blind god of love, without braille, with only bow and arrow, through the art of archery, can release love literature as the crow flies, from the abyss of the heart even of the dog to the cat without missing the target, making even two sworn enemies two sworn lovers (Gesticulates). But can he invoke the coincidence of two damsels scampering at the same hour into the ventricle of your heart in obedience to him? That curious coincidence was arranged. You must have sent for her to get our

113

hackles up So that we may hack each other to pieces, a sport for you to gloat over as testimony of your being a sought–after gem.

Tell me young man: is she not your fiancée?

LANRE (interrupts with humane Superiority):
-I'm not affianced to anybody yet. Don't mind that noodle who will not accept "no" for an answer. Is it possible for me to marry all the dolls who fall in love with me?

LADY (quaintly)
-Don't you love her?

LANRE (peremptorily):
-She does not fit into the mental picture of my life-partner. Every man has a woman made from his rib, out there, meant for him, waiting to be discovered, fixed back into position to complete and complement him. That is his Miss Right.

LADY (moving closer to him, kisses him fanatically, clinging to him):
-Lanre, I love you.

LANRE (moving nearer to her too, returns the kisses frantically):
-Darling, I love you too.

LADY (almost begging him, with a gleam of desire in her eyes):
-Am I the negative of the picture your mind paints of your life-partner?

LANRE (loftily):
-As the graft fits into the stock so you fit into my idea of a partner.

LADY (relieved, then affectionately):
-Am I your Miss Right? The one made from your missing rib? Am I the only person in your life?

LANRE (disarmingly):
-I swear by my birth, you are.

LADY (smiling coquettishly as she embraces him):
-I do not take your words with any grain of salt.

LANRE:
-My word upon it.

LADY (with child-like awe, looks up to him, longingly):
-But what about the pregnancy I told you about?

LANRE (momentarily bewildered, then with a wry face):
-You suggested you're going to do something about it: terminate it.

LADY (capriciously):
-That is a sensible thing to do, isn't it? Considering that I'm yet to complete my education and we are not yet psychologically and financially ready to settle down.

LANRE (eagerly):
-How much will that cost?

LADY (coaxingly):
-Some thirty thousand Naira.

LANRE:

-That's rather expensive. In some places, it costs as little as ten thousand Naira.

LADY (eagerly, with gleams in her eyes):

-That is with the quacks. But I'll go to a standard clinic with competent and experienced hands, sterile 'everything', no unnecessary management and guaranteed safety.

You know, 'Life has no duplicate' and cannot be bought with money. So, preserving it can never be said to be too costly.

LANRE (concurs with her):

(Counts out thirty-five thousand Naira)

-Well, you are right on that score.

(Hands over Naira notes to her)

It is getting late. I'll run home.

(Walks towards the door)

I will see you tomorrow.

(Lady follows him, waves)

Till then, take care.

(*Exits*)

LADY (soliloquizing)

-Heigh-ho!

(Walks about, shaking her everted head, flinchingly)

These creatures: men! mugu! maga! malu!

They can do anything to avoid responsibility. How easy it is to deceive them? With this same pretext had I extorted money from one rich man and so will I from another one.

Curtain falls

ACT ONE. SCENE FIVE

Men love the luxury but not the responsibilities of having women.

RHAHAAB'S APARTMENT
The atmosphere is gloomy. The apartment is in a middle-class estate. Lanre knocks, waits for a long interval before the door opens.

RHAHAAB (Forlornly. In her night-gown, in front of the door, angrily, almost shouting):
-Oh Lanre! So, it's you? Are you the fulfilment of the prophecy? The fulfilment of the prediction that seven women shall take hold of one man, saying, we will eat our own bread, and wear our own rai-ment. Only let us be called by your name, to take away our reproach?

LANRE (begging her to lower her voice, apologetically):
-Rhaa, it is not like that. It is not what you think.

RHAHAAB (with an impression of girlish insouciance, drearily):
-But in your own case, the very perfection of the prophecy, seven women will kill themselves for one man to bury their reproach, as preordained.

LANRE (conciliatorily):
-No woman is foreordained to die for me.

RHAHAAB (pointing to her scars, bitterly as she strolls in, flippantly):
-Have you not killed me already? You've broken my heart, rubbished my pride, humiliated my ego, wounded my esteem, dampened my spirit, buried my hope and

117

roasted my soul. What is left? My head aches. My face, neck ache.

(Turns her back to him)

That currish whelp of a wife of yours (walks towards a chair) nearly killed me.

LANRE (interrupts, follows her in, genially):
-She is not my wife. I'm young and single.

RHAHAAB:
-Tell that to the marines.

(Both sit down)

She must be! The way that wench wrenched and wriggled me from you, then pounded me, like the king of beasts, she whacked me. (Demonstrates)

One fell thwack after another, as with pestle and morta, she pounded me, at least she must be your fiancée. Don't try to run with the hare and hunt with the hounds. You like dark-skin girls, you like them short and plump, but must you sample all girls? Must you go the whole hog and peruse the internal anatomy of all the varieties of female homosapiens before your choice? Toaster of all, tester of all, "taster" of girls, at the end will you settle down with all? Can you minister to the needs of all? Polygamist, is that your choice? Is she not your fiancée?

LANRE (duplicitously):
-I have not plighted my troth to anybody yet. In truth, she is not my fiancée.

RHAHAAB (wistfully):
-If I had known it were so I would have taught that Lily-livered girl the lesson of her life. But, 'had-I-known' is an afterthought that always comes too late.

If she is not your wife, why did you leave us to fight to the bitter end?

LANRE (didactically):
-I had to; lest I should be accused of taking sides.

And my input could have poured fuel on the fire and so aggravate the tension. I did not say anything since least said soonest mended, nay, in such a situation, speech is silver, but silence is golden.

In fact, I came to apologize to you.
(Gets up and stands over her, paternally)

For that incident which must have hurt your feelings.

RHAHAAB (looks up to him, intently):
-After the double whammy? Why the apology? Do I mean anything to you?

LANRE (as if he rues that day they fought, smiles wistfully as he glances at her):
-Yes! You mean everything to me.

RHAHAAB (tormentedly):
-Your blarney again? Flatterer don't play upon my heart strings. How many girls mean everything to you? To how many of them have you recited that hackneyed song before?

You once told me you love me. But today, what does that gage mean to me other than this smirch, this scar on my face which continues to rankle in my mind?

LANRE (Walks around her, apologetically):
-On my honour, you and only you mean everything to me. You are my choice, the only one I love.

RHAHAAB (taken aback, stares unbelievingly at him, with her left hand on her waist, her chin rests on her right wrist, grandiloquently):

-Am I the one you love? What type of love? A mug's game? A passing fad? Cupboard-love? Or is it calf-love?

Without prospects? Without a purpose? Save beer and skittle? That's for Kiddies' Puppy-love. At my age, settling down in a home as man and wife, and knuckling down to the task of raising a family should be the goal.

LANRE (meditating gloomily):

-Should we not better start off as lovers and know each other fully? Than start as husband and wife only to find out, at the end of the day, that we are incompatible?

In every amour there is a purpose. Love-affairs are like planted grains of mustard seeds. In a rocky soil, they wither like grasses in the hot summer. But in a fertile soil, nursed by patient and dedicated tenders the prospects are as bright as the Hibiscus flower.

RHAHAAB (with bitter levity):

-In the process of nursing a love-affair patiently, what if I were gulled? After you'd have had your fill of me I'd be dumped like an obsolete article, thence-forth to try again, hoodwinked by men's selfish proverbs that there can be no prospects without a trial.

LANRE (cunningly):

-It's a parallel axiom: nothing ventures, nothing gains. In every enterprise there's a risk. But in this case, the bond of affection acting as our bond of fair play, the prospects outweigh the risks.

RHAHAAB (ambivalently):
-Especially in this our case, this our affection, this our nexus combined with the child between us - it binds us in one knot as husband and wife. It compels a speedy wedding to give legitimacy to this bud of our graft.

LANRE (astonished, pensively):
-Which child?

RHAHAAB (stands up, walks towards him, convivially):
-I'm carrying your baby, whose expected birth adds to the weight of why we should stop experimenting with school-type amour and settle down in a blessed home in preparation for the task which our parents did on us: the task of nurturing our offspring as our time is ripe.

LANRE (walks away, leans on the window, stares into the distance, as if trying to see into the future, resolutely):
-You need to terminate that pregnancy.

RHAHAAB (vehemently): Filicide?
-No! I cannot do a thing like that. If I kill this one, am I sure God will give me another one?

LANRE (convincingly):
-Why not? You have to do away with this one until we are ready to settle down for family life.

RHAHAAB (determinedly):
-I'm ready to settle down now.

LANRE (threatening):
-Then, you have to find another father for that child. You have to find a man who is ready to father children now.

RHAHAAB (holds his hand tenderly, with gleams of affection):

-Are you suggesting that I should give your child to another man to father?

LANRE (with cool impertinence):

-I'm not responsible for this pregnancy. I'm not the father of this child.

RHAHAAB (scandalised):

-You are responsible for this pregnancy. Who else?

LANRE (freeing his hands from her grip):

-We will do paternity tests.

RHAHAAB:

-Do paternity tests for what?

LANRE (walks away, speculatively):

-Do paternity tests to exonerate me from false accusation.

RHAHAAB (following him madly):

-Did we do tests when you were begging me to open my legs? Did we do blood tests when your sweaty body was bumping and grinding away as if you must get results by all means?

LANRE (walks out through the door, with full measure of finality):

-Then, I'm not responsible for that pregnancy.

(*Exits*)

RHAHAAB (shouts after him, reproachfully):

-Oh! You men! Callous creatures. Your specialty is hit-and-run. Our desperation is your weapon. Your targets are us, frail creatures.

And the flotsam and jetsam of your heartlessness are the shoals of hapless public children, the waifs and strays without future, without fathers, without faith, even in nature for they're without nurture.

Curtain falls.

ACT ONE. SCENE SIX

Women's competition for husbands is the real world example of the spiritual Kingdoms' competition for human souls, both wars are as difficult as boiling the ocean.

A SCENE IN RHAHAAB'S HOME
The apartment is typical of a place rented for a rich man's mistress. It is artistically furnished. Music is faintly heard in the background, otherwise it's deadly quiet and lifeless. We see Rhahaab reclining uncomfortably on a sofa. On her face we can readily read, boldly written: 'Forlon Hope'. In her eyes we can see gleams of repeated trials at getting this elusive thing which her heart most craves for.

We are still trying to contrast between the extreme beauty of her face and figure, her gorgeous environment and lofty bearing with the overwhelming worry and fear of never getting her heart desires cemented on her face.

(Rose enters in a hilarious mood. She embraces RHA-HAAB rapturously, laughing and snuggling against her)

ROSE (singing, dancing as she sways her hips at her hostess, cheerily):
-Our big tommy mama, it is now quarter to. When's the expected date? (Embraces Rhahaab again and again)

RHAHAAB (wincing as she is embraced, happily, with the Pan Am smile):
-In a few days' time, my fair-weather friends Have left me in the lurch. I am displeased with you and your sister.

For almost a year now you've refused to see me because the mountain cannot go to see Mohammed, and out

125

of sight is out of mind. Or is it because I ate the forbidden fruit and became heavy?

ROSE (laughing jovially):
-Auntie! We are not that bad, my sister has gone to Saudi Arabia.

RHAHAAB (Puts her left hand on her waist, adjusts her posture with difficulty, surprised. Inquisitively):
-Saudi Arabia! Without telling me? Why? What happened?

ROSE:
-Hmm! A little problem, that her boyfriend, the handsome young doctor, has broken her heart.

RHAHAAB (more surprised, wonderingly):
-That young doctor? My friend was certain of marrying him.

ROSIE (sitting down beside her, philosophically):
-Men are not only chameleonic but really unpredictable! My sister was virtually living with him. My parents, his parents, everyone had approved their relationship, and they were getting prepared, bit by bit, for their eventual marriage. And then! Hmm.

RHAHAAB (Adjusts her posture again, attentively):
-And then what? I'm all ears. What happened?

ROSIE (genuinely distressed, facilely and effortlessly):
-My sister just woke up one morning to find out that he has gone to Saudi without even telling her, his would-be better-half.

126

RHAHAAB (aghast, drily humorous):
-Gone to Saudi Arabia. What for?

ROSIE (didactically):
-Oh! They are just using their oil money to slap us in the face, as if we have no oil. With our crippled health care system, they now poach our rich patients and buy over our doctors, so our poor are bereft of health care.

RHAHAAB (grimly):
-What has your sister done about this?

ROSIE (narrates effusively):
-She has gone over there to smoke him out. She said they are so far involved with each other that he cannot now withdraw and leave her as a victim of the current use-and-dump syndrome epidemic.

RHAHAAB (vexed in the spirit, sighs):
-Gone too far, beyond the point of withdrawal, beyond the point of return. Poor Lady, that is a wise thing to do.
We, too, must be tough with these heartless men.

ROSIE (fondles her):
-Aunty, what about the would-be father of your expected child? Has he owned up to his responsibility?

RHAHAAB (chokes with suppressed anger):
-He has to! You know these proud cocks with their usual bold front. But his child is his child, there are no two ways about that. What about your friend, Beki?

ROSE (still stroking her belly, blankly):
-Oh! That poor soul: she is now in a psychiatric hospital.

RHAHAAB (dazed, showing more interest):
-Tell me: what psychiatric hospital? What took her there?

ROSE (despairingly):
-Another victim of men's heartlessness. She lost her heart to a callous man who had the temerity to heap coals of fire on her head, which made my poor Beki out of her very right mind.

RHAHAAB (breathless, despondently):
-O-oh, all these men, these devils that women need in their lives, a hateful-lot. How did it happen?

ROSE (Explains painfully):
-Whilst she was still in school, her boyfriend, a young businessman, came to her father and plighted his troth.

The old one, in his sagacity advised the plighted lovers to wait until his daughter had completed her schooling.

The impatient proud cock did not buy the idea and told Beki in no uncertain terms that year was his appointed year for marriage.

Beki tried to make the he-man see reason with her old man, all to no avail. Before she could make up her mind, whether or not to disobey her father, on one sunny Sunday morning, when she went to church to worship her God, she met this man, without the slightest inkling, with a woman, pledging, for better for worse as he led the woman to the altar.

Her mind so reeled at this unexpected shocking find that she blackened out. That trance lasted seven long days. And when she came back to life,

(*A toddler noisily enters the room. Rose gets up, carries her, and walks about as she talks*)

128

It was without her memory. When all hope was lost, the harrowing experience which obfuscated her memory released but one remembrance. The awakened reminiscences of their love affairs. She was lovelorn, my ever-cheerful friend was pining for unrequited love.

'I want my Johnny! (The toddler complains, tries to get down to her auntie) to be in his arms, kissed, caressed by my lover. I want my Johnny - she kept shouting - as furious as a rabid dog, for days on end.

Without food, without water, without any other memory, not remembering even myself, her closest friend, nor her mother, nor her father - she kept barking, with hot glittering tears. 'I want my Johnny'.

My friend was lovesick.

RHAHAAB (Rose hands over the baby to her, forlornly):
-Pity! Poor little thing. Men! How cruel? How brutish, beastly and arrogant, how unpredictable, how elusive, how unfeeling, how hard on our frail selves?

ROSE (slowly, painfully and profoundly):
-That was not the pitiful part of it. The part which rends the heart, makes one to lose balance and arouses rancour is that these men are deaf to their still, small voice. Languishing in the psychiatric hospital, my once spirited Beki, day after night and night after day, my love-struck friend,

(*The baby toddles out of the room, dragging along flowers in a pot, unnoticed. The pot breaks into pieces*)

out of her right mind howled: 'I want my Johnny to sit beside him.' The doctors, versed in the curative art of insanity, and conversant with insane minds, treated her sick mind in futility. Exasperated at failed attempts to douse the inflamed mind, they sent for Johnny, as an experimental curative, that his presence may feed her starved mind, a balm for her agitated senses, and a douche to douse the flame of her choking passion.

He came: his arrival was the magic cure. Balmy as it was, it heralded the return of calm to my violent Beki. First, her memory returned as she recognized first Johnny, then her parents and then us, her bosom friends.

And so, life returned into her ramshackle shell as she ate and smiled and thought like human beings. We were all buoyed up with new hopes. Impressed, the seasoned healers of infected minds insinuated that Beki should live with Johnny for an experimental short while (Sits down opposite her) to see if she can achieve complete recovery from her mental ill-health.

With a snigger the brute bragged: 'What do you want me to do in my house with a mad woman?'

And turned his back, into a waiting car off he went, mindless of the casualty of his brutish act.

RHAHAAB (overwhelmed, compassionately):

-Whew! Without the slightest compunction? These men are as hard as nails. Tell me, I pray thee, prithee, what then happened to the pitiable patient?

ROSE (with suppressed gesture of despair, emotionally):

-She flared up and became as mad as a March hare. This compelled the Alienists, as a last resort, to treat her with electro-convulsive therapy, which wiped off her memory all traces of learned facts.

And now, though calm, my once brilliant friend, still not quite compos mentis, goes about unable to learn things as simple as ABC.

130

RHAHAAB (with bitterness):

-(Her brother enters, waves and eyes Rose, whispers into her ear: I "dig" this your friend oh. She shouts: 'Take your eyes off her. You males are all the same, burning charcoal on our labile bonds'.)

(The brother dashes out)

This hurts, this wound hurts. It tempts one to take up arms and shoot off all these men. These men's cruelty is why I earlier on advised you to take occasion by the fore-lock.

Have you met your Mister Right?

ROSE (suddenly in high spirits, gleefully):

-Yes! I have! I have met the man of my dreams! Dozens of men woo me every day of the Lord, but none has ever so tickled the fancy of my heart.

None has ever so moved the tendrils of my feelings. None ever so seemed so right to me before. But he is as elusive as the heavens is to the puffed-up old Nick.

I was not so sure I seemed so right to him, I had to sail even near to the wind to catch the fancy of my heart.

RHAHAAB:

-Aha! Went that far?

ROSE:

-Yes. It was my bounden duty.

RHAHAAB (pryingly):

-How? What did you do?

ROSE (fudging the issue, reluctantly):

-I went to the shrine to obtain philtre for him.

FLASH BACK

Lights fade in the forestage, thunder is carried over loudspeaker, as from a distance, with an interlude of black-out before lights brighten on forestage again, where Rose stands in the shrine, trembling.

A short stool covered with white cloth has a voluminous book Kept in opened position by long keys on it.

Lights fade again on forestage as arrays of burning candles make flaunting buntings and variously coloured feathers conspicuous in the shrine.

Amidst thunder, lightning, clangour and uncanny noises stands Rose shaking in-front of the shrine. Beside her stands the shrine's angel clad in white robes all over, except his eyes. His garment is as white as snow and the hair on his head as white as wool. With a holy book in his left hand, a bell in the right, the shrine's angel clangs his bell. Everything here is in slow motion.

THE SHRINE'S ANGEL (bows reservedly):
(In a meditative pose, after a pause. Clangs his bell, kranang, kranang)

-My Lord! My Lord! My Lord! The sun rises from the East and sets every day in the West because, like the clock, you have set it that way.

The Earth spins on its axis, revolves around the sun, hangs in the balance, baths in the space, brings forth day and night, all at your command.

Whatever goes up, falls down, all from your power.

The shooting star scuds across the sky and then disappears because you have designed it that way. Great is thy work, everything is made by you, whatever happens is by your permission, who is like unto you? Whatever you have determined, who can change it? Times, seasons, life, death, all are prearranged by you.

(As violent cold wind makes candle-light dimmer; peals the bell, bows again)

My Lord! You commanded: 'Go, multiply and fill the Earth'. 'Live as husbands and wives' Then you established the institution of marriage, the perfect example of how humans should relate with you, total submission and dependency in exchange for total protection and to instruct us to submit and be dependent to escape being devoured or violated as we live as husbands and wives. You teach us by what we see around us. What you have cast is set.'

(Lights up slowly on him; bows again and again, peals the bell)

My Lord! Your obedient daughter here (points to Rose) has seen the man of her dream. May you join them together. And what you have joined together may no one put asunder.

(Rings the bell)
My Lord! With you all things are possible.

(Sudden *black-out. Silence, intense silence that instils fear hangs over the Shrine for some minutes. No light, no sound and no motion. Pulseless pause*)

THE SHRINE'S ANGEL (His clerical garb shimmering, falls on his knees, then, dim light slowly brightens on him, hands clasped and raised to high heavens, face squeezed in agony and eyes focused on high heavens):
-(Tinkles the bell) My Lord! Have we thy servants sinned? We are all born sinners. We only thrive on your boundless mercies.

Did you not say: 'Ask and it shall be given unto you'? All forgiving God, forgive us our sins and answer to our supplications.

(*An uncomfortable silence follows. thunder, lightning, clangour and uncanny noises, everything shakes*)

(*Amidst this, the voice of the Lord is carried over loud-speaker, as from a distance, slow, loud, clear but deafening*)

THE LORD'S VOICE (from above, roaring angrily):
-The gods are angry. Femininity has been desecrated. It was meant for procreation. They now use it as bait. They now use it for advert. They now use it for entertainment.

Bottom power has been misused. They now trade it for money, to put food on the table. They now barter it for wealth, to buoy up their economic power. It is now an instrument for fraud. Bottom power has been defiled.

They now use it for achievement. They now use it for power.

Bottom power has been abused. The gods are angry over the profanation of the procreational endowment by women. It was designed for human perpetuity but has been debased to profanities. Seduction prowess has been mis-directed.

(*As the voice fades, thunder, lightning, clangour and uncanny noise rise to a crescendo and become deafening*)

SHRINE'S ANGEL (slowly and painfully, looks up with awe, raises his arms in half supplication, clangs the bell. Noise ceases):

-My Lord! Benevolent God! Benignant God! We're at your mercy. What shall we do to appease the gods? Go to church every day? Host non-stop vigil?

Rectitude all we've gained from abuse of bottom power? Sacrifice goats? Do dry fast for seven times seven days? Stop the abuse of bottom power?

(*After a brief pause, thunder, lightning, clangour and uncanny noise rise to apogee. Appalled, everybody trembles. Everything shakes. Amid this, the voice of the Lord comes again, petrifying, slow but clear*)

THE LORD'S VOICE (roars, pauses after every point, chillingly):

-Do you know how much water has passed under the bridge? Can you tell how many people have become barren from sexually transmitted diseases due to misuse of bottom power?

Can you count the number of children that have been bastardized by this indiscretion, the abuse of bottom power?

Do you know how many babies have been aborted?

Can you count how many women have been buried from abortions following misuse of bottom power? Do you know how many doctors are residents of hell from "pre-babicide"?

Can you count the rivers that have turned crimson red from abortion blood? Can you measure the seriousness of this sacrilege? This is the pull of the dead foetuses on heaven, the cry of foetal blood to heaven.

This is why whatever goes up must come down. This is why sexually transmitted diseases are rampant nowadays.

This is why infertility is soaring.

(Everywhere is eerily quiet)

THE SHRINE'S ANGEL (getting more worked up. Everything stands still initially then, shaking for the first time, he raises his eyes to high heavens):
-(in a loud voice) So, what do we do my Lord?

THE LORD'S VOICE (roaring frighteningly, then unsettlingly):
-Do nothing! Do nothing!! Do nothing!!! The gods have since fore ordained that there shall be marriageable men everywhere, wedding bells ringing every time, wedding gowns strewn over every place but not everything in skirts, not all nubile girls on earth, shall ever be in them –m-m-m-m! (eerily)

Because they have desecrated womanity, not everything in skirts shall ever have a husband, not every woman on Earth shall be a wife. Not every woman on Earth shall ever know peace.

Because they profaned womanhood, there shall be wombs everywhere, but not every womb on Earth shall ever shelter babies. Not every woman on Earth shall ever be a mother. Not every breast on Earth shall ever suckle children.

Because they have debased femininity, women shall be used, even by beasts.

Because they have traded their dignity, women shall be inferior, below, beneath....in subservience: the disobedient has been sold to evil manipulations and depravity. m-m-m-m.

(*Rose runs off, with a cry trailing in an echo. Lights slowly fade out on the stage as roaring voice fades. Full light back on stage where we see Rose again with Rhahaab, cool music still wafting from the inner room*)

RHAHAAB (Rose is seen still shaking):
-So, you failed to obtain the love portion?

ROSE (sighs heavily, still slightly visibly shaken, with eyes distended):
-Fear, freezing fear, drove me out of the shrine empty handed.

RHAHAAB (pricked, aside):
-So, this is why, for women, getting married is as elusive as the wind. It is inherited punishment that makes some women never to become wives or mothers. Now dicerns that it is curse to womanhood that peace eludes some women - handed down punishment.

(To Rose) Are you worried that you might be one of those pre-destined to see with the eyes, touch with the hands, long for, but never be apparelled with a nuptial gown?

ROSE (touched, now understands why some women find marriage as elusive as the shadow):
-My heart trembles, though I was not specifically mentioned but, if it were so, if they say "marriage is not for every woman", I would fight against the judgment of the gods. I will fight to vacate the verdict of the gods.

RHAHAAB (aside):
-It is easier to boil the ocean than to change the consensus of the gods. Is it possible for humans to be free from the gods? (To ROSE) These people, these nitwits, have they not predicted before that the world will end some years back? Today, are we not nearly certain that life on earth has no end?

Put your mind at rest, and don't be bothered by empty words of ordinary mortals like ourselves.

Are you sure you really needed the philtre to win him?

ROSE (dryly):
-Well! These men, one can never say 'never' with them.
In this matter, they are like the branches of trees that can be swayed by the direction of the wind.

RHAHAAB (curiously):
-Doesn't he feel about you the same way you feel about him?

ROSE:
-I am not so certain. I've warmed myself into the cockles of his heart, but if another lady insinuates herself into his favour, he might sway.
How can I be sure whether as he is right for me, I am also right for him? How can I tell whether as I hunger for him, he also hankers for me?

RHAHAAB:
-Didn't you put your mind across to him?

ROSE:
-I did! Indeed, I did! I enticed him to make a policy statement on the future as it concerns us.
RHAHAAB:
-What was his mind?

ROSE:
-He was evasive. His words were pregnant with meanings and liable to sundry interpretations. He spoke from the two sides of his mouth. Men are as labile as their promises.

RHAHAAB:
-What was his promise?

ROSE (ambivalently):
The promise of a man to a woman is like a covenant, always with a proviso. The promise of a man to a woman is like the promise of a child, to tell their visitors that his mother, who is sleeping, has gone out.

He will surely say to the visitor: 'My mother who is sleeping inside the house said I should tell you that she has gone out'.

Thus, keeping his promise to his mother but failing her.

RHAHAAB:
-What were his words?

ROSE:
-He said: 'If only I could wait until he gets a job, owns a comfortable accommodation, owns a car before he will think about marriage.'

RHAHAAB:
-Truly, his word indeed has many meanings, like a sword capable of cutting from any of its edges.
By the time he will decide to think about marriage, did he tell you what his mind will be as it concerns you?

ROSE:
-No! Even if he did, by then his mind may change. The colour of the chameleon changes as many times as its background changes.

So does the mind of a man: it changes as many times as the number of new girls that he meets.

RHAHAAB:
-Will you then wait for him?

ROSE:
-Wait for him? The world will end before he gets a job. When lawyers, engineers and doctors roam the streets endlessly in search for jobs, when will he, a graduate without a profession, poor fellow, get a job?

RHAHAAB (sonorously):
-Don't wait for him, my dear Rose. Time waits for no woman. Women grow old sooner than their age; we are like the flowers: in the bloom with the morning dew.

Shining with the rising sun. Brimful of evanescent beauty with the morn air but seared ere sunset. Time waits for no woman.

It is not myth that women wither before they die, women actually wilt before they get old. And become unproductive before then, and so unmarriageable after due season.

(*Enters the same brother again. Hands over a note to Rose. Rose reads, smiles*)

ROSE:
-I have so decided, Auntie.

RHAHAAB:
-Any other men in your life?

ROSE:
-Wooers. They come ceaselessly and stick like leeches to me. But they all want one thing with me: nice time. Nil else.

RHAHAAB: (to the brother):

-Stop hovering around here, she is not for a 'casanover' like you.

(To Rose) None nearly serious?

ROSE:

-There is this billionaire who owns a business empire.

He begs me to marry him every day. It is as sure as fate that he is as serious as a verdict.

RHAHAAB (brusquely):

-And what is holding you back, lucky girl? Grasp at that opportunity.

ROSE:

-No, I can't marry him. (Exits the brother)

RHAHAAB (philosophically):

-Money! Class! Prospects! What else does a woman want in a man? Consider the comfort, overseas tours, important connections. With a flip of your finger anything you want will be at your disposal. Don't let this slip you by.

ROSE (presumptively):

-He is not my idea of a husband. He is not my Mister Right. If I had a choice, it would not be him.

RHAHAAB:

-This concept of Mister Right is baseless, that every man has a woman made from his rib, foreordained as his wife. It is proved wrong now that some men decide never to marry.

Where are the women made from their ribs? What happens to the women made from their ribs?

ROSE (conjecturally):
-The major reason is that this man has six wives and wants me as his seventh.

RHAHAAB (curtly):
-A multi-millionaire can take care of a hundred wives. A million at your disposal. It is life annuity for the fling of your life. Take time by the forelock.

ROSE:
-The cat-and-dog life with the other concubines over-shadows the lure of millions.

RHAHAAB (hypothetical):
-Quarrelsome life is the life of the needy because a hungry person is an angry person. Millions are the douche of such life.

ROSE (judgementally):
-The dive is as bald as a coot and as dull as ditch water.
As his scalp is bare of hair so is his face bankrupt of beauty and his figure barren of attractiveness, as the old fogeyish man's paunch distorts his frame into an apish man.

RHAHAAB (opines):
-Beauty is only skin deep. Handsome is that handsome does. Are you going to marry fashion or the hair on a man's head or the flatness of his belly?
Isn't marriage a venture? And, like all other enter-prises, isn't what one gains out of it, one's benefits, the only thing that matters?

ROSE:
-He is not ideal for me as a partner.

RHAHAAB (submits):
-A man can wait for his ideal wife, it's never too late for them. But women, without time on our side, we can't wait for our ideal husband, we only marry who is willingly to help us beat Old Father, Time. We do not marry because of love but because we have to. We marry whoever is ready when we're ready, lest we become over-ripe, rejected and frustrated.

ROSE (walks to the door):
-Consider our age difference. He's at the last score of his lifespan now. I don't want to be widowed ere forty.

RHAHAAB (with difficulty, follows her to the door):
-When we cannot see beyond the horizon, cannot peer into nor forage the future's dark abyss, cannot illuminate the depth of the unknown, even with divination; when we do not know how long we'll live or when we'll die, how can you tell when another person will die?

How are you sure your death knell will not toll before his? Only God knows when He will summon us, pawns of fate, mere mortals at His mercy: the wheat to gather and store, the tares to gather and burn, to cut and thresh, to straw and grains, the straw to gather and burn to ashes, the grains to sift to heaven and the chaff to winnow to hell, our ado amounts to cinders. All only pared down as has been set down.

ROSE (with finality):
-My Mister Right is out there. I will wait for some years. If I have an option, I will not.

RHAHAAB:
-Are humans, mere tools of the spirit-kind, given options or choices or do they, upon the only chance, flaunt

143

Hobson's choices laden with conditionalities and threats of the consequence of disobedience, bordering on compulsions that human frailty cannot but flout because the conditionalities are tantamount to duress or choicelessness?

Before we were formed, shaped and knitted in our mother's womb, they knew us; without our counsel, set us apart and ordained us, even in our limitation, the election to their Glory.

They, without negotiations or our input, lend us our lives, assign our gender, origin, the colour of our skin, our role in life; and where and when we are born; they order our footsteps, decide what we turn out to be and where and when we will die.

Is it weightier things like who we will marry, or whether or not we will marry or end in heaven or hell they will leave for humans to choose? Did we choose before we were created? When we were conceived or born, did we choose? Instead of the illusion of choice, is Morton's fork not better than the dilemma of humanity?

The spirit-kind decides the fate of humankind. They fix us at our time, in our course and lane and settle us in our place - in peace or pieces, blissfully or blastfully, mere appurtenances of their Glory - and brainwash us into believing that our destinies are in our hands whereas humanity is the ping-pong game of the gods, pilloried among the gods, plumaged and deplumed by the gods, pounced on until won as trophy into either of the opposing kingdoms of the gods.

ROSE (volubly):
-All are created on spec. Each is specced to purpose, creatures play their assigned roles, serve their purpose: the sun lights the planets, the rivers water their banks,

144

rain wets the land upon which the flowers spread their fragrances that scent everywhere, the nectar feeds the bees that make honey which sweeten our food and heals our infirmities, plus the trees' fruits on which humans feed, enough inducement for human-kind to serve the spirit-kind, with all bowing down in worship, declaring the power and proclaiming the glory of Nature. But even so, spiritual control will not extend to our mundane dalliances with each other in nature's designed service chain and web of interdependence. The gods will not choose husbands for us - if you want to say that old married man is chosen by the gods for me. I reject the destiny of marrying that old married man. It is not my portion (they both laugh)

Curtain falls

ACT ONE. SCENE SEVEN

A bastard has no family rights.

A SCENE IN RHAHAAB'S MOTHER'S HOME
We see a large family house with a moderately furnished sitting room. The air is cheerless and there are no signs of happiness or celebrations.

(Rhahaab's mother is sitting in dejection, her chin on her palm, depicting failed hope and expectations. Rhahaab enters, with her baby)

RHAHAAB (pensively):
-Mummy, why do you look sad and depressed? Is it because the father of my baby has never shown up to catch the first blush at his son?

RHAHAAB'S MOTHER (dejectedly):
-That bothers me too but not as much as the disturbing dream I had last 'noon, which bodes us no good.

RHAHAAB (hands over the baby to her, forlornly):
-Mid-daydream is a sign of fatigue. What was it about?

RHAHAAB'S MOTHER (meditating, gloomily):
-I was not tired. From my youth, even in those halcyon days of yore, I do not drowse away a hot afternoon. But that strange noon, I was hardly seated when I slept off and hardly asleep when I saw this baby perched on a golden chair.

Then from the canopy of heavens fell a star so glittering that it dazzled the gazing eyes. Gingerly, gingerly, gingerly, it fell, till it nestled on the temple of this innocent babe.

RHAHAAB (sits down, relieved but grimly):

-Is that then what bodes ill for us? A star on the temple of a babe on gold?

RHAHAAB'S MOTHER (changing countenance, tormentedly):

-What portends that the child will be a sport of fate is the cockfighting which aroused me from the dreamy sleep.

It turned the cockles of my heart into boding. When I coddle this lovely baby (coddles the baby) my mind reels as I revisualize the sudden appearance of two cocks by the sides of the chair with him and the star on his head.

As if obeying the whistle of the umpire, the cocks started the sport for the onlookers. With their hackles up, one pecked at the other and the other at the one. They pecked and pecked and pecked and pecked, again and again and again and again, they pecked and pecked, till one could only totter to its feet as the pecking by the other removed a dozen of its colourful feathers.

After the pecking by the one tore into shreds the peony-coloured cockscomb of the other which could only trudge as it was 'punch-drunk' and had become too weak from loss of blood from its torn cockscomb.

RHAHAAB (enters a cat, curiously):

-And what were they fighting for?

RHAHAAB'S MOTHER (the cat notices a dog in the same sitting room, insipidly):

-The star on the head of the baby. First, the one which blushed as red as peony pecked the star from the child's head, and then the other from the one and the one from the other till the force and confusion of the struggle put the star back on the head of the baby.

148

The pecking continued without the umpire's whistle, with the star changing position from the temple of the baby to the beak of the one to the beak of the other.
With a confused rhythm, the cycle continued till the fear of the child losing the star called me out of that visionary scene.

RHAHAAB (enigmatically):
-How interesting some dreams can be! See how brain fag can make the mind to be in a whirl, the vortices of which conjure up figments of the imagination we see as dream, an emptiness, of no significance, occasionally glamorized by coincidences.

RHAHAAB'S MOTHER (half incredulous, fearfully):
-Dreams in one's salad–days, when one dreams of developing wings and soaring like an eagle or being chased by the old serpent, may have no significance.
But at my age when the placid mind has been sobered down by happenings, each dream is a vision, an omen, a reflection of the past as it portends the future.

RHAHAAB (Rhahaab's father, wearing a long face, passes through the sitting room without saying a word to anybody):
-(Eagerly) So mummy, what does this mid-day cock-a-doodle-doo mean?

RHAHAAB'S MOTHER (with a gesture of despair. Ominously):
-It is not cock-a-doodle doo at dawn. The spirit-kind is bipolar - with a loving, caring and preserving facet and a fiercely fiery devouring facet. In wrath, before they destroy, they warn. Dreams, visions and prophecies are the

149

main media through which Divinity forewarns and fore-tells humanity. That was why I went to Kpa-okodio to seek the meaning to that odd hour-dream.

RHAHAAB (sceptically):
-Is he a clairvoyant? A sorcerer? A diviner? A sooth-sayer? An astrologer, or the Great Joseph? How are we sure that if we go to another person we will not have a different interpretation?

RHAHAAB'S MOTHER (snorted, derisively):
-He is a man of great powers. From clairvoyance to invocation with extrasensory perceptions. He does all sorts of extraordinary things.

The year I gave birth to you, it was over that piece of land that they now mine precious stones from, the Aros hired mercenaries from Ahofia. In multitude the troops arrived for the coup de grace in the Pogrom over the pro-tracted polemic over a land pregnant with shekels, a land the blood of our past heroes has oiled the tendrils of our firm grip.

But before their arrival, our people saw the straw in the wind. While I was petrified by the fear of losing your father in the imminent war, our elders sent for Kpa-oko-dio to obviate the impending danger.

Kpa-oko-dio, the link between the living and the dead. Aged and senescent but not senile, and still spry, a man, as deaf as door mail and as blind as a bat, who sees with his walking stick, who also reads people's minds from the construction of their knitted brows, a dumb person whose actions speak louder than words. An intermediary between humanity and Divinity, even though dumb, but by his gestures, communicates signals from the spirits, even though blind, but deciphers messages from our

150

ancestors, feeble but shares authority with the deity, and from his wisdom envisions tomorrow.

He came. And what did he do? He only dropped one coconut at the entrance of the village for his only price of a virgin girl. At night the soldiers arrived. We all woke up to see our enemies kicking the coconut about as football.

From dawn to dusk, the game lasted uninterrupted. Then, suddenly a dispute erupted between the two teams of the same troop over who should go home with the coconut ball. From argument with mouth to might and main with matchets and cudgels they hewed themselves into pieces.

Even, the last of them to die committed suicide in spite of our people begging him to return to his mother.
'No! I must die!', he stood his ground, he cried before falling on his sword. And, since then, that oil-rich land has remained indisputably ours.

RHAHAAB (shocked, then convinced):
-He does have extra-ordinary powers.

RHAHAAB'S MOTHER:
-How else does Divinity showcase power but by delegating power to spiritual beings and then to intermediaries like Kpa-okodio?

RHAHAAB (now understands, and is convinced):
-What did Kpa-okodio say is the meaning of your dream about my child?

RHAHAAB'S MOTHER (unpropitiously):
-That the child has two fathers, which I find most unusual and unsettling.

RHAHAAB (protests loudly):

-Mummy, nobody on earth ever had two fathers, except you mean the earthly father and the heavenly father, making two for everyone. Otherwise, my child only has one father.

RHAHAAB'S MOTHER (teasing her with searching scorn, inauspiciously):

-And you said he has a father?

RHAHAAB (confidently):

-Yes, of course. Every human being has a father who brought him forth. Did I make the child alone, in a crucible, in a laboratory?

RHAHAAB'S MOTHER (probing further, lips curled in disdain):

-(Gets up to go inside as the baby starts crying) Why hasn't the father shown up till now?

RHAHAAB (following her, persuasively):

-He will. If he doesn't, the toils of the law will catch him. I will compel him in court to own up to his responsibilities.

RHAHAAB'S MOTHER (choking with suppressed despair, in derision):

-I can only keep my weather eyes open.

Curtain falls.

ACT ONE. SCENE EIGHT

Supplimentary wives have no marriage rights

A SCENE IN ROSE'S HOUSE
A sprawling magnificent estate in a government residential area- GRA. One mighty building is centrally located in the compound with other smaller ones well arranged around the main one. In front of the main building is a terrace and behind it is a beautiful garden. This rich man's compound is completely fenced round - with an imperial façade.

(A rasping rap on the door wakes Rose up. She sleepily makes her way to the door and opens it with slight difficulty)

ROSE (in her night gown, as if sleep walking, reverently):
-Mama Ibe, good morning.

MAMA IBE (shouting raspingly):
-What is good about this morning? I have warned all of you before, all the other so-called wives have heeded my warning. But because you think you are nearer to his heart, since men, once they see a new woman ignore the old ones until the new one becomes old too, are heedless of my warning.

I am warning you for the last time. In any coronation, launching or any ceremony that there is an invitation for Chief and Mrs. Udechukwu,

None of you must ever show your faces on the high table. If you do, I will drag you down from whatever height and in which ever gathering you may be.

ROSE (with a dozy dreamy, disturbed air, indignantly):
-Why?

MAMA IBE (irritably):
-Oh! You don't know? Or you don't want to respect tradition that has been observed ages before you were conceived? Because I am the first wife and so, the only recognized wife: Mrs. Udechukwu.

ROSE (retorts, still indignantly):
-What about his other wives?

MAMA IBE (cocks a snook at her contemptuously):
-Who are his other wives? One man, one wife: that is the law of the creator, the design of nature and the tradition of humans. All of you, the other women: concubines, mistresses, side-chicks, baby-mamas, whores, you are just paid to assist me in satisfying his needs, period!

ROSE (losing all self-control, defiantly):
-He paid bride price on me just as he paid on you. So, I am his wife, just as you are. Any rights you have as his wife, I also have the same measure of same rights as his bonafide wife.

MAMA IBE (stands nose to nose with her, rhetorically and gesticulating appropriately):
-You are not ashamed to share another woman's husband. You are not ashamed to eat my leftover. I finished all the milk in him before you appeared on the scene to lick the pus of my contamination.
Have you ever asked yourself who toiled and moiled for the money you are enjoying today?

Have you ever asked yourself who built the home you are basking in now? Have you ever asked yourself who made up the man in whose favour you are basking in now? Have you ever asked yourself who laid up the luxury you are wallowing in now?

(She draws out her words) I, Nnene, the daughter of Ekanem, a woman among women, made Chief Udechukwu, what he is today, not just because people say: 'Behind every successful man there is a woman'.

(She draws on and on, thumping her chest) But without me, my very self, the unseen pillar behind the sky-scrapper, he would have been a church rat today. And you wouldn't be here now showing your teeth to the sky and shouting: 'His bo-o-n-a-f-i-i-dee wife.'

For that singular reason, I deserve absolute respect and unrivalled position as his only wife, while you girls, Shut up your traps and 'chop' the money you did not work for.

(Rose listens on with suppressed anger) You all came after money. I left that to you because I have enough. But it must stop at that. Why didn't you find a young man and build with him from the scratch a home you can rightly call your own?

You wanted a ready-made home, and you still have the guts to say, like a man with a cleft-palate, 'I am his wife'. You cannot serve God and Mammon - be virtuous and greedy, serve two masters. You cannot be another woman's husband's fuck-buddy and still have a right to a husband. You cannot be adorned with the garment of shame called supplementary wife number seventh and still be anointed with the protection offered by marriage. An aberration.

(*Mama Ibe said this with her fingers in her nostrils while breathing through the mouth and at the same time swaying her hips at Rose*)

ROSE (animated. Can no longer control her temper. She heaves a sigh):
-S-s-s-s-s-s-s-s-s-s-s-ch, See me ooh. I was sleeping peacefully; trouble came to wake me up. Nonsense. (And turns her back, to go into her house)

MAMA IBE (Furiously takes her head-tie off her head; ties it round her waist to support her wrapper):
-Moi? Me? My very self?
(Thumps her chest gravely) Who is old enough to be your mother? And has given birth to two of your type at the same time? Because we share one man, one community prick, because you are 'baby-sitting' my husband, you have seen me through like a transparent glass. Do you see no sense in me?
(Holds Rose firmly with her two hands and forces Rose to turn back and face her squarely) Are you biting the finger that feeds you? Are you rubbing salt on the wound you've already caused? Are you the cow which has a tail but does not know how much it depends on it? Are you the ungrateful mad dog which dares to turn back, bark and bite its master?
Brat! Chooser, bagger of curses! Accursed of Divinity. By the time I finish with you today you'll regret the day of your birth. You will know that sharing a husband does not make us age-mates but only prick-mates. You will know that the mouse does not dare the cat to the boxing ring. You'll know that you can enter my womb now and I deliver you cut and dry. For daring to barb the lion's

beard in his den, I will settle your hash today. First, I'll give you a black eye.

(*Rose, choking with suppressed anger, wrenches herself from Mama Ibe's clutches. Mama Ibe slaps her in the face. Rose returns the slap. The two exchange blows, crying and abusing each other. Rose feels highly embarrassed, summons all her energies and gives her assailant a vigorous push. Mama Ibe falls many times as she tries to get up after the first fall from the hurl*)

MAMA IBE (Glares back, incensed, still trying to get up, breathless, disparagingly):
-The God of old age will not allow this hussy to disgrace her mother's age-mate.

(*Rose feels highly embarrassed, flounces away, then runs into her house, slams the swinging door shut and hurriedly locks the door*)

Running away? Come outside! Let me give you the recipe for hunting for your own husband. The wood insect dares the fowl. Let it venture out and see if the fowl will not pick it up and swallow. You will know that opening your legs for another woman's husband does not guarantee the privilege of protection offered by your own husband.
A child who refuses to show good manners outside usually learns how to do so in his mother's cooking pot.

(*Rose refuses to come outside; Mama Ibe cleans herself and leaves*)

ROSE (weeping, lies on her bed as glistering warm teardrops roll down her eyes, lamenting):

157

-Yesterday, the first and the second wives quarrelled because all the former's children are in schools in Zurich, while the latter's children here at home pine for such an opportunity.

And today, again, here I am, fighting for the first time in my life without any red rag. Quarrels, bitter quarrels every day. Fights, envenomed fights every time. War to the knife. Jealousy, envy, smouldering hate. Is this the type of life I chose (rolls about on bed), to fight all the days of my yet unspent life?

And what was the lure of this harrowing life? Money? Desperation? Impatience? Could I not have found my own husband? Could I not have been better off on my own, single, free, living a life with peace of mind?

Even, this so-called marriage, I was denied what my heart most craved for, the adornment with the bridal gown. The pomp of the wedding ceremony. The motorcade, the singing, the dancing, the discussions with my mates about the best moment of my life, with the review of the video-film of that monumental moment, peoples' sanction, church's sanction, God's sanction, which crowns the solemn ceremony, the ceremony of all ceremonies to the feminine mind. And why was I denied this apple of my eye?

Because the society says only the first wife of a man deserves that honour, that recognition, that sanctification. Then I am not his wife. I am not recognized by the society as his wife. What am I then?

(Gets up, pants about) His bedfellow? A fucking hell mate? His wives' maid? His children's nurse? A number in his household? An article for his admiration? A spare or reserved fuck buddy -a friend with benefits - without any label? Or an object of scorn?

(Hears her husband's voice as he ambles towards her house) Let him come! Let me find out from him today what part I'm playing in this life's drama. Did I choose this role or was it foisted on me?

CHIEF EDECHUKWU (tall, huge, thick, broad-chested, high-spirited, as merry as a grig, calls out, affectionately):
-Rosy, Rosy, Rosy. Are you alright? What is the matter, oh?
(*No reply*)

Rose darling, Rose darling. (As he struts through to her house)
Are you not in?

(*No reply*)

(*Chief Udechukwu knocks on her door. After a short delay, Rose eases open the door and runs back to the bed still sobbing*)

CHIEF UDECHUKWU (in wrapper only, waltzes in, apologeti-cally):
-My dear, I heard you have been upset this morning.

ROSE (In an apartment that is luxuriously and artistically furnished. Reticently, still shedding tears):
-Don't call me your dear.

CHIEF UDECHUKWU (genially holds her, wiping tears off her face):
-Why? My dear, why?

ROSE (with queasiness):
-Am I your wife or am I not? Tell me, I pray you.

CHIEF UDECHUKWU (soothingly)
-Why? What type of question is that? You have seen a goat lying stiff in death, and you still ask: 'is that goat stone-dead?'

ROSE (with gauziness):
-Answer me in plain language, I pray you, not with quibbles having double meanings.

CHIEF UDECHUKWU (balmily, sits beside her on bed):
-What else do I tell you, my dear?
ROSE (with her face down, puts the pillow on her head to hide her face, insultingly contemptuous):
-What part am I playing in this your life's drama?
a) fucking hell mate?
b) fuck buddy?
c) friend with benefits?
d) friend without label?
e) screw mate or just an instrument of torture?

CHIEF UDECHUKWU (taken aback):
- What sort of 'JAMB'[5] question is that?

ROSE (insolently):
-Point of correction. Post 'UME'[6] question. Am I or am I not your wife?

CHIEF UDECHUKWU (mellowly, runs his fingers over her neck, tenderly):
-You? The most beautiful of all women. You, my most prized possession. You? The nearest being to my heart.

---

[5] Joint admissions & matriculation board
[6] University matriculation Examination

Don't mind Mama Ibe. She only said that with her tongue in her cheek.

ROSE (wistfully):
-Have you been treating me as your wife?

CHIEF UDECHUKWU (paternally):
-What do you mean, my beauty? What do you need that I have not given you? Money? How many millions have I not given you? (Teasing her affectionately) Do you want more? Just say it.

Mention any thing you want: cars, houses, clothes, jewels, what? I'll give them to you right now.

ROSE (lifts up her head. Looks into his eyes, intently):
-How many days in a month do you spend with me as your beloved wife?

CHIEF UDECHUKWU (demonstratively, counts with the fingers):
-There are twenty-eight days in one month. I spend twenty-one of those days in twenty-one different nations of the world where I have business concerns: otherwise, the money won't keep tumbling in.

I'm left with only seven free days, and I have seven wives. I spend one day in a month with each wife. What more can I do?

ROSE (sits up on bed with him, snorts with rage at him):
-Is only one day in a month with one's husband enough?

CHIEF UDECHUKWU (obviously offended):
-Young woman, I am a single human being, not two. Can I divide myself?

161

ROSE (breaks down and weeps loudly):
-What type of life is this? My God, what misfortune is this? Fate! How unfair! How cruel! See what you have foisted on me.

CHIEF UDECHUKWU (infuriated, haughtily):
-Young lady, did you say living in my house is a misfortune to you? Did you say being my wife is a buffet to you? If you cannot cope with me, leave. That is the way out. (Points to the door)
I will marry another woman before you even make up your mind to pack out.
(Rose cries louder than before) I came home to rest, to rest with peace of mind. Since you women will not allow me to have that now, I'm leaving. I'm going to Toronto now! Tomorrow, I will be in Trinidad.

(*Exits*)

ROSE (still sobbing, bemoans):
-Here, I have money. This vile money which decoyed me into this crass neglect. Money that cannot buy peace of mind. Money that cannot buy happiness. Money that cannot fill this vacuum, this vacuum of desires. (Muses)

(*Then she hears a tap on the bedroom's rear window, turns round and sees a man peeping in through the window, heartily*)

He has travelled out of the town. Turn round and come right inside.

(*The man turns around and enters*)

You don't look your usual self. What is the matter?

THE ENTRANT (suspiciously):
-I'm afraid.

ROSE:
-Afraid of what?

THE ENTRANT:
-This is dangerous.

ROSE:
-We won't be caught. I'm alone, lorn grass widow now.

THE ENTRANT (stoops over her, paternally):
-I don't want to be caught. Because if I am caught, I will lose my job and lose my livelihood. As a driver, to get a new job now is almost impossible as only few people now buy new vehicles.

(*Sits down on the bed beside Rose as she signals to him*)

ROSE (flirtatiously):
-I now understand why you have changed. Six months ago, you used to walk in confidently. And always on time. But for the past few months, you have been as timid as a rabbit. I assure you that we will not be caught.
And if the worst comes to the worst, I shall change your position from my driver to the driver of my friend or pay you life annuity.

(*Rose puts her hand into his reluctant hand*)

THE ENTRANT (persuasively):
-At stake is my job as well as my life. If an important person is killed, the press will be interested. To the sky

will they shout till the minions of law have fished out the 'assassins of press' interest.

But if an unknown fellow is killed, it will make news as much as the death of a fly in the human kingdom. Should my 'Oga', your husband, find out our enterprise, it will be as easy as ABC for him to kill me.

ROSE (whimsically):

-No, he cannot go that far. God knows, he has not discharged a husband's duty to his wife. And I'm bound to live, at least as a woman. He knows he cannot meet our needs and only stops short of arranging co-bed mates for us. He pretends he does not know that we all have stand-by arrangements to supplement His inadequate supply of our needs.

(*As Rose pulls him towards her, pictures fall out of his shirt's pocket. Rose picks them up, looks at them unbelievingly, shouts*)

Ah! What are these? Pictures of you and I, nude! Blackmail?

THE ENTRANT (stiffly):

-No. Not blackmail. I cannot do a thing like that to a nice lady like you. I am in trouble. My senior brother who works in a custom's office bribed an official to transfer him to the 'roadblock' where he can make a lot of money.

But he was caught and charged to court and may end up in prison. I cannot let him stew in his own juice. I need some money to bail him out of this trouble. If I were sure of getting the money from you, I would not have gone as far as taking these pictures.

If you can give me fifty-thousand Naira, the picture and negatives are all yours. If not, I will be pushed to the wall to raise some money, because I cannot live and see my brother hauled off to prison.

ROSE (satisfied):
-You should have told me that instead of this hanky panky. That would have saved you the cost of this picture. Bring out those bundles of money from that chest-drawer. (Points)

(*Entrant makes a dash for the chest-drawer, opens and looks unbelievably at its contents. He Takes out two bundles of notes and hands them over to Rose*)

Take this: fifty thousand. And don't be mischievous again.

ENTRANT (happily):
-Thank you. I can always rely on you, beautiful lady.

ROSE (smiles, gestures imperiously):
-Bolt that door. Don't dawdle away time. Come over and rapture me now.

(*He closes the door, returns to her on bed, falls into her opened arms, her lips move towards his*)

Curtain falls.

ACT TWO. SCENE ONE

Bride price confers paternity but DNA confirms paternity

A SCENE IN THE COURT
The Court room is full. The proceedings are in mid-session already. We see RHAHAAB in the witness box.

LAWYER:
-What is your name?

RHAHAAB:
-Miss Rhahaab.

LAWYER:
-What is your residential address?

RHAHAAB:
-10, Uben Edem-eyen street, Edem-urua village in Iwerre clan, Ini Ical Government area of Akwa-Abasi Ibom state of Nigeria.

LAWYER:
-Whose baby is that in your arms?

RHAHAAB:
-My baby.

LAWYER:
-Who is the father of that child?

RHAHAAB:
-Lanre Aso.

LAWYER:
-Who did you say is the father of your child?

RHAHAAB:
-Lanre Aso.

LAWYER:
-And why are you in this court now?

RHAHAAB (fluently):
-I brought forth this baby together with Lanre and since the birth of the child three months ago the father has refused to take the responsibility of bringing up his child.

I came to plead the court to compel Lanre, as the father, to take responsibility of caring for his child, having made me to bear a child for him, and consequently preventing my getting married to any other man. The court should compel him to marry me or pay compensation for damages done to my person and my future.

LAWYER (feeling as if this is a 'bread and butter case', as merry as an eel, gestures to his colleague):
-My learned friend, you may cross-examine my client.

DEFENCE LAWYER (jumps to his feet, formidably):
-Miss Rhahaab, that is your name. Am I correct?

RHAHAAB:
-Rhahaab is my name.

DEFENCE LAWYER:
-How many men do you know?

RHAHAAB (thinks briefly, then offhandedly):
-I know my father, I know my grandfather, I know my uncle and cousins. I cannot give the exact figure for the number of all the men I have known since I was born.
(*Murmuring is heard in the background*)

DEFENCE LAWYER:

-Of this uncountable number of men that you know...

LAWYER (springs to his feet with alacrity):

-Objection, my Lord. My client did not say that she has met with an uncountable number of men but that she cannot remember the exact number of men she can be able to recognize, which is natural.

JUDGE (amused, smiles):

-Objection sustained.

DEFENCE LAWYER:

-Of this multitude of men, how many of them know you?

LAWYER:

-Objection, my Lord. The question is irrelevant, an unpardonable intrusion upon my client's privacy.

JUDGE:

-Objection sustained. Counsel, change your course of questioning.

DEFENCE LAWYER:

-Is this child your first and only child?

RHAHAAB:

-Yes, sir.

DEFENCE LAWYER:

-Did you sleep with any man, other than Lanre, at any time during the period of about nine months before the birth of this child?

LAWYER:
-Objection, my Lord. The answer may be an embarrassment to my client.

JUDGE:
-Objection is overruled. The answer is relevant to the determination of this case.

DEFENCE LAWYER:
-Did you sleep with any man, other than Lanre, at any time during the period of about nine months before the birth of this your child?

RHAHAAB:
-Yes, sir.

DEFENCE LAWYER:
-How many men did you so know?

RHAHAAB (furtively glances at her counsel):
-I cannot remember.

DEFENCE LAWYER:
-Five, ten, fifty, hundred. Just make an estimation.

COUNSEL FOR THE PLANTIFF:
-Objection, my Lord. My learned friend is holding my client up to ridicule.

JUDGE (nods):
-Continue with your question.

DEFENCE LAWYER:
-How many men slept with you within the period of nine months prior to the birth of this child?

RHAHAAB (looking down, ignominiously):
-I cannot remember.

DEFENCE LAWYER:
-But you slept with not less than one man, other than Lanre within the period of nine months prior to the birth of this your child?

RHAHAAB (hesitantly)
-Yes.

DEFENCE LAWYER (posits):
-I put it to you that you made this baby together with any of those men you met at that period other than Lanre.

RHAHAAB (protests):
-No! This suckling is Lanre's.

DEFENCE LAWYER:
-Have you ever seen a widow who is also a mother of many children who gets married several years after the death of her husband?

RHAHAAB:
-Yes.

DEFENCE LAWYER:
-Have you ever seen a divorcee and mother of many children who eventually gets married to a new husband?

RHAHAAB (begrudgingly):
-Yes.

DEFENCE LAWYER (winningly):
-Have you ever seen a girl who drops out of school because of pregnancy, gives birth to a child, and returns

to school after a period of time to complete her education?

RHAHAAB:
-That example is very uncommon.

DEFENCE LAWYER:
-In other words, having given birth to a child does not prevent a woman or a girl from getting married and does not constitute a damage to her future.

(*Everyone in the court-room murmurs, some in agreement, others not, with the advocate*)

RHAHAAB:
-It does, sir.

DEFENCE LAWYER (triumphantly):
-I have no more questions for her.

JUDGE:
-You may return to your seat.

DEFENCE LAWYER:
-I now call on the defendant, Mr. Lanre Aso.

COURT OFFICER:
-Lanre Aso is called to the witness box.

(*Lanre mounts the witness box*)

COURT OFFICER:
-What is your religion?

LANRE:
-Christianity.

COURT OFFICER:
-Take this Bible in your right hand and read this.

LANRE (takes the Bible in his right hand and reads):
-The evidence I shall give shall be the truth, the whole truth and nothing but the truth.

DEFENCE LAWYER (winingly):
-Have you ever seen the plaintiff before?

LANRE:
-Yes.

DEFENCE LAWYER:
-How many times have you seen her before?

LANRE:
-Today in this court is the third time.

DEFENCE LANRE:
-So, you have seen her only twice in your house.

LANRE:
-No! Only once in my house and once in her house.

DEFENCE LAWYER:
-Why have you not taken responsibility for the child which the plaintiff said is yours?

LANRE:
-Because I'm convinced that the child is not mine.

DEFENCE LAWYER:
-So, you have failed to claim that child because he is not yours?

LANRE:

-Exactly! Besides, I had sexual contact with the plaintiff only once. She is only palming another man's responsibility off upon me.

DEFENCE LAWYER (turns to his colleague, suppressing a smile):

-You may cross-examine my client.

COUNSEL FOR THE PLANTIFF (jumps to his feet, tactfully):

-Mister Lanre Aso, you have seen Miss Rhahaab only twice before?

LANRE:

-Only two times before today.

COUNSEL FOR THE PLANTIFF:

-How long did you spend with her in your first meeting?

LANRE:

-I don't know exactly.

COUNSEL FOR THE PLANTIFF:

-How long did you spend in your second encounter with her?

LANRE:

-I don't know, as I did not go there with any chronometer.

COUNSEL FOR THE PLANTIFF:

-Ten minutes, one hour, one day? Just make an approximation.

DEFENCE LAWYER:
-Objection, my Lord. This question is irrelevant, and is a waste of time for the court.

JUDGE:
-It is a simple question. Let him answer.

COUNSEL FOR THE PLANTIFF:
-Just estimate the duration of your meeting in the two instances.

LANRE (recollecting):
-The first one was a whole weekend.

COUNSEL FOR THE PLANTIFF (artfully):
-Does that mean from Friday to Sunday, inclusive?

LANRE:
-Yes sir.

COUNSEL FOR THE PLANTIFF:
-What about your second encounter?

LANRE:
-About three hours.

COUNSEL FOR THE PLANTIFF (leading him on):
-When was this, twelve months ago, that is, nine months before the birth of that child in the plaintiff's hands?

LANRE:
-Yes, sir.

COUNSEL FOR THE PLANTIFF:
-How long does it take a man and a woman to make a baby together?

LANRE:
-I don't know.

COUNSEL FOR THE PLANTIFF:
-Just proffer and estimation, from your knowledge of elementary science.

DEFENCE LAWYER:
-Objection, my Lord. My client is not an expert on human reproduction.

JUDGE:
-Objection is overruled, because the answer requires common sense. Your question again.

COUNSEL FOR THE PLANTIFF (tricksily):
-Is it possible for a man and woman sleeping together for one hour to make a baby from such an encounter?

LANRE (reluctantly):
-You may be right.

COUNSEL FOR THE PLANTIFF:
-Is it possible for you and Miss Rhahaab to have made this baby together when you spent three whole days together?

LANRE:
-But...

COUNSEL FOR THE PLANTIFF (brusquely):
-Just answer Yes or No.

DEFENCE LAWYER:
-Objection, my Lord. The answer amounts to jumping to conclusion.

JUDGE:
-Just answer whether it is possible or not.

LANRE (stammers)

COUNSEL FOR THE PLANTIFF (curtly):
-I put it to you that you could have and did indeed, make that baby together with Miss Rhahaab during that long weekend you spent together.

(*Everybody in the Court room suppresses their infectious impulse to murmur*)

Curtain falls.

ACT TWO. SCENE TWO

Two sperm cells can never fertilise one egg, two penises can never simultaneously enter one human orifice, two fathers can never sire one child, all signposting the fact that humans can never serve the Supreme and the Supramundane beings at the same time.

A SCENE IN THE COURT
We meet the court in full session. The Court room as well is full to capacity. Everyone listens on with rapt attention

COURT OFFICER:
-Mister Ette is called to the witness box.

(*Ette confidently mounts the witness box*)

What is your religion?

ETTE:
-I have none.

COURT OFFICER:
-Will you like to affirm?

ETTE:
-Yes.

COURT OFFICER:
-Lift up your right hand and read this affirmation.

ETTE (lifts up his hand and reads):
-I affirm that the evidence I shall give shall be the truth, the whole truth, and nothing but the truth.

(*JUDGE signals to the counsel*)

COUNSEL FOR THE PLANTIFF:
-Doctor Ette, that is your designation, am I right?

ETTE (ebulliently)
-Yes.

COUNSEL FOR THE PLANTIFF:
-What are your qualifications?

ETTE:
-B.Sc. (Laboratory Technology), M.Sc. (Human Physiology), PhD (Human Genetics).

COUNSEL FOR THE PLANTIFF:
-How many years of working experience do you have to your credit?

ETTE:
-Twenty years.

COUNSEL FOR THE PLANTIFF:
-How many of those years have you been actively involved in the determination of paternity disputes?

ETTE:
-Fifteen years.

COUNSEL FOR THE PLANTIFF:
-Are you conversant with the details of this case?

ETTE:
-I'm fully aware of the details of the case.

COUNSEL FOR THE PLANTIFF:
-Have you seen the child whose paternity is being disputed in this court now?

ETTE:
-Yes.

COUNSEL FOR THE PLANTIFF:
-Have you seen the child's mother in this court today?

ETTE (points):
-Yes.

COUNSEL FOR THE PLANTIFF:
-Have you seen the defendant in this court today?

ETTE:
-Yes! I have seen him. He is sitting over there. (Points)

COUNSEL FOR THE PLANTIFF:
-What did you do with them: the child, the mother and the defendant?

ETTE:
-I took blood specimen from each of them.

COUNSEL FOR THE PLANTIFF:
-What did you do with those blood specimens?

ETTE:
-I subjected the blood specimens to analytical tests for inherited blood substances called genes.

COUNSEL FOR THE PLANTIFF:
-What did your tests show?

ETTE:

-The tests confirmed that the child whose paternity is being disputed has blood 'genes AB'. The child's mother is blood group B, and the defendant is blood group A.

COUNSEL FOR THE PLANTIFF:

-How does an individual come by this blood substances?

ETTE:

-These blood substances called genes are invariably passed down, that is, inherited from, and only from, both parents of an individual.

COUNSEL FOR THE PLANTIFF:

-What does the results of the analytical tests you carried out on those blood specimens mean?

ETTE:

-The results mean that the child whose blood was tested inherited the blood gene B, from the mother and inherited the blood gene A from the father.

COUNSEL FOR THE PLANTIFF:

-Are there any other ways of interpreting these results?

ETTE: \
-No! all disciplines of human Genetics are unanimous on this modality of inheritance.

COUNSEL FOR THE PLANTIFF:

-And you said, "The child inherited gene A from the father?"

ETTE:

-Yes! Since the child's mother does not have the gene A in her body, the child inherited the gene A from, and only from the father.

COUNSEL FOR THE PLANTIFF:

-And you said "The defendant has blood gene A?"

ETTE:

-Yes! The test confirmed that the defendant has blood gene A.

COUNSEL FOR THE PLANTIFF:

-How many people did you take blood specimens from on the day you took blood from three of them?

ETTE:

-Only three.

COUNSEL FOR THE PLANTIFF:

-How many blood specimens were in your laboratory on the day you carried out the tests?

ETTE:

-Only three.

COUNSEL FOR THE PLANTIFF:

-So, you could not have made any mistakes? You could not have mistaken another person's blood specimen for the defendant's?

ETTE:

-No! I labelled the specimens as soon as they were taken.

COUNSEL FOR THE PLANTIFF:
-My Lord, these laboratory reports marked Exhibit B1, B2 and B3 may be received in evidence.

(*Hands over the reports to the Judge, who scrutinises them, before handing over to the defence counsel. Satisfied, the defence lawyer returns the paper to the Judge. Judge purrs his approval as court clerk receives the exhibits*)

My learned friend, you may cross-examine the witness.

DEFENCE LAWYER (springs up):
-Mister Ette, what did you say are your qualifications?

ETTE:
-PhD. Human Genetics, M.Sc. Human Physiology, and B.Sc. Laboratory Technology.

DEFENCE LAWYER:
-How many sexually active males are there in the world?

ETTE: (shakes his head vigorously):
-I don't know.

DEFENCE LAWYER:
-By your estimation, are there more than one million sexually mature males in the world?

ETTE:
-You may be right.

DEFENCE LAWYER:

-Assuming there are one million sexually active males in the world, what percentage of that population has the blood gene type A?

ETTE:

-About forty-two percent.

DEFENCE LAWYER (calculates on a piece of paper):

-That is, about four-hundred and twenty thousand sexually active males have the blood gene type A. And I'm sure the world's population is more than one million and such males are more.

ETTE:

-By mathematical extrapolation from scientific estimation, ...yes!

(*An atmosphere of infectious uproar is created as everyone burst out laughing*)

DEFENCE LAWYER:

-In other words, the child whose blood you tested could have inherited the gene A from any of the four-hundred and twenty thousand males, or any of the males with the gene A in the world?

ETTE:

-The child could have inherited the gene A from any of the fertile males in the world with the gene A, whose intercourse with the child's mother resulted in the pregnancy, whose delivery resulted in the child.

DEFENCE LAWYER (exasperated):

-My Lord, I have no more questions for him.

JUDGE (relieved, to the witness):

-Thank you very much, you may return to your seat.

(To the counsels) You may now summarize your cases and address the court.

DEFENCE LAWYER:

-My Lord, the case before this court is to prove beyond all reasonable doubts that my client is the father of the plaintiff's child. And that, the counsel for the plaintiff has failed to do woefully.

For instance, there is ambiguity as to who donated the gene A, the inheritable substance, to the child, from among all the men in the world with that gene.

You should therefore exonerate and discharge my client for want of evidence and lack of diligent prosecution.

COUNSEL FOR THE PLAINTIFF:

-My Lord, the case before this court is not to determine how many men in the world have the inheritable substance A or the science of how many of them the child could possibly have inherited it from.

Nor is it the duty of this court to determine how many men my client has known or could possibly know. All available evidence, as given by the plaintiff, the defendant and the genetic tests, are conclusive in proving that:

the defendant did meet the plaintiff, and the result of that meeting is a child who inherited an inheritable substance A, among all other inheritance genes, from the defendant.

The case before this court now is to, within the provisions of the law, hammer into the head of the defendant that, since he and the plaintiff jointly made a child, they should jointly shoulder the responsibility of giving nurture to the child.

Failing this, the court should, within the provisions of the law, compel the defendant to live up to his own responsibilities, not to shirk the responsibilities he knowingly incurred.

With his eyes wide open, he put his hands on the plough. He has bitten the food into his mouth. Now, he must chew what he has bitten. I don't believe he has bitten more than he can chew.

Does he now want to leave his bite for the plaintiff alone to chew for him? Is that fairness? Is that justice?

(*Everyone in the Court room is talking at the same time, most of them, in agreement with the last speaker*)

Curtain falls.

ACT TWO. SCENE THREE

Among the fathers (bride price father, foster, legal, deadbeat, DNA and acknowledged father): there is the confirmable father, the bio-dad, instantiating the fact that besides the gods there is one true God.

A SCENE IN THE COURT
Another day, we meet the court mid-way in session. We are greeted by loud silence. As usual, the court room is full to capacity.

DEFENCE LAWYER (uninhibitedly enthusiastic):
-My Lord, on behalf of my client, the defendant in this case, I pray the court to grant permission for the case to be withdrawn from court for an amicable settlement at home. Both parties to the case have consented to this arrangement.

JUDGE (clears his throat repeatedly):
-I have received your timely application for withdrawal of the case from court for settlement. But what the parties to the case should be concerned with and the settlement efforts must be based on the fact that it has been proven beyond all reasonable doubts in this court that the defendant did know the plaintiff in a procreative way.

The defendant and the plaintiff now have a child between them and that this knot is that of shared responsibilities.

These salient facts should be the basis of the settlement. I therefore adjourn this case pending the outcome of the settlement effort.

Curtain falls.

ACT THREE. SCENE ONE

Human life has been pre-programmed in such a way that unless humans exclusively serve their creator, they are destroyed by other gods, spirituality represented by an actual concrete example, personality: unless a woman becomes a wife (exclusively exploited but jealously protected by her husband), she will be indiscriminately exploited and violated by all men.

A SCENE IN ROSE'S HOUSE
Rose, lying on a sofa and looking at the ceiling as she ruminates over recent events in her life

(Alice enters)

ROSE (as Alice enters, adorably):
-Oh! My Pretty lady! Your round cherubic face is beautiful. Your outfit is gorgeous. Your appearance is cute. You are up to date and fashionable, the centre of attraction of all men. Queen! Your crown is coming, your king is on his way. Welcome to my poor home.

ALICE (dances to the music in the background, delightfully):
-My wonderful friend. How magnificent your home is. You are in fortune's lap. Here is heaven on here below.
Life could not be more wonderful. How jealous I am?

ROSE (gets up humorously, and in riddles):
-Grace is free, unexpected, undeserved, generous, favourable, loving, clement, spontaneous, saving, salving, sufficient, more than needed, yet with thorns, the "Thorns

191

of Grace. So is the Hibiscus flower: beautiful, decorative and yet with thorns.

No home is perfect, no life is blight free. Is all that glitters perfect? Are precious glittering gemstones not also spiky and pricky? We all carry our cross, make do with our Fate and are content with our lot.

Don't kill me with compliments. What can I offer you: orange, pineapple, drink or whisky?

ALICE (sits down, sedately):
-Don't let me bother you with more than what brought me here. I need some help from you.

ROSE (impatiently):
-What type of help? It's my obligation.

ALICE:
-I need some money from you.

ROSE (sits down, calmly):
-Like how much money?

ALICE:
-One million Naira.

ROSE:
-What do you need that much money for?

ALICE (bemoaning her lot):
-I can no longer stand the taunting of my well-wishers, stomach the jeers of my colleagues, endure enemies who poke fun at me over my inability to catch a husband and savour the flavour of marriage. Every day, everyone gets at me over this leprous stigmatisation of my status of singleness. Opportunity knocks but once, they say. I met a young graduate who has a big problem. If I can get that

amount, I'll use five hundred thousand to solve that his problem and five hundred thousand to rent an apartment and shelter him now that he is stranded. Opportunity knocks but once, they say.

ROSE:
-What are you being that Good Samaritan for?

ALICE:
-So that once he is out of the woods, he will feel so indebted that he will be forced to marry me.

ROSE:
-What if he refuses to marry you in the end?

ALICE:
-Then I will force him to pay back the money. Even if we have to go to the Court for that.

ROSE:
-He might pay back the money.

ALICE:
-Where will he get that amount from? He can't even dream of getting a job.

ROSE:
-That is a good idea. It is very important for every woman to get a husband by every possible means, even if all the man can do for her is to drive away flies.

Any woman who fails to catch a man early in life is paving way for loneliness in old age, and will spend her latter life fighting infertility. The standards, times, roles and expectations for women are different from that of men. The lie, the unlimited freedom, the rebellion, the disobedience, the fruit that humans were hoodwinked into accepting (eating) is absolute freedom (feminism). These are truths feminism fails to highlight to women.

Women cannot do without men; they have been pre-programed to be dependent on men right from the level of the gene.

ALICE:
-That is the burden of the modern-day lady. Man conveys the privilege of protection on womanity. But why is this so?

ROSE (deeply):
-Besides genetics and spiritual programming, you have the hormones, chemistry, physiology, anatomical and psychological needs. This is the way providence demonstrates and showcases the fact that, as humans must depend on their maker for survival, so are women dependent on men for peace of mind, fulfilment and freedom from indiscriminate defilement and violation.

ALICE:
-I understand the underlying principles now. I have come to the knowledge that women must depend on men. I must do everything to get a husband that I shall recline on because this is a man's world: man gives origin to woman - he is her foundation. Man is the suffix of woman. Mr is the prefix for Mrs. Females are formed from males. First, the world was made and handed over to men. Millennia after, as an afterthought, without even asking for it, women were made and given to men. It is indeed men's world.

Do you want to write she? You must also write he. He is her root, her all.

Menarche signposts the onset of priming of girls for men and when men start eyeing young girls the way they ogle women. Menstruation is the 'lunarly' cleansing of the thoroughfare for men. Menopause is when men pause making eyes at women who pause being attractive (useful) to men.

Woman, women, menarche, menstruation, menopause all indicate that women are created for men or without man there is no woman. Without he there's no she. Without him no her. Like Nature, the indispensability of men to women is not in doubt. Even Madam and I'm Adam are palindromic.

Besides, as the human body has been preset, like an alarm clock, to eat and defecate, drink and urinate, to inhale and exhale, so has human Life been pre-programmed such that unless humans are protected by their creator they will be devoured by other gods, spirituality represented by an actual concrete example, physicality, unless women are covered by the protective cocoon of their husbands they will be indiscriminately violated by all men.

As it is in the heavenly template, its duplicate, in this men's world, women are clay casts of men, created from, and for and cocooned in men, otherwise they perish, as humans, likeness and image of their maker, are created by and dependent on their creator otherwise they perish. So, the same way hunger pangs gnaw one to food, will the need for this protective cocoon coax me into my husband's hands, a man that I shall serve as my master or I shall perish.

For if it has been predetermined that the huge Earth, settled on the pillars of its foundation, is still tilted on its axis, and further set on a spinning course, yet still primed to rotate about its axis and operated remotely to revolve round the Sun, then what a privilege for a woman to be only required to serve and be exploited exclusively by her

195

husband. Her head. Her lord. Her lot. Her cocoon - much to her relief from indiscriminate exploitation by all men, and symbolising humans, as preset in subjection and subservience to the gods. The exploitation and violation of women by men is only an instantiation of the subjection and subservience of humans to the gods; neither feminism or divorce nor quest for independence can unset what has been preset by the gods. I shall have no qualms serving my husband for rebellion shall never prevail against the fiat of creation. And only marriage can give me protection, happiness and peace of mind. So, I must get a husband by all means.

ROSE:
-Can you come tomorrow after I might have returned from the bank?

ALICE:
-Why not? Gratefully so.
(A knock, the door opens, a man enters) I'll be running along. See you tomorrow.

ROSE (sees Alice off to the door, with their heels clacking away as they walk across the tiled floor):
-Bye, beautiful one (waves)

(*Exits Alice*)

(To the entrant) Why are you late again? Still afraid of being caught?

THE ENTRANT:
-Yes.

ROSE:
-He has travelled to Germany again.

(*Both walk into the bedroom*)

THE ENTRANT:
-What about his other wives? They might tell him if they discover our secret affair.

ROSE (as both sit on the bed):
-You want me to narrate to you what they have been doing? We all lack intimacy and exclusive bond with our husband. We are starved of man's companionship which we cannot do without and so, we all have 'stand-by' arrangement for the supply of the needs of our souls. He meets them once a month too.

(Throws her hands round his neck) And no woman can survive on that. The first wife sleeps with her night guard every day. The second wife sleeps with her steward.

THE ENTRANT (hands over a sealed envelope addressed to Rose):
-This is for you.

ROSE (curiously tears open the envelope and scans what she brought out of it):
-Nude picture of you and I again? Another blackmail attempt?

(The entrant stands up, walks towards the window) You and who are behind this thing?

THE ENTRANT (leans on the window, stone faced, answers with dead silence)

ROSE (crisply):
-How much money do you want this time?

THE ENTRANT:
-One million Naira. (Looks out through the window absent-mindedly)

ROSE:
-In cash or cheque?

THE ENTRANT:
-Raw cash.

ROSE:
-When do you want it?

THE ENTRANT:
-Right now – before any... (as he turns to face her)

ROSE (flares up, indignantly):
-Report me to him: I'm not paying you any money! I'm fed up with you men, gilded devils, Done with all you sour grapes. (Sits up, slowly but indignantly, looking at him, eyeball to eyeball)
Fed up with this gilded pill called marriage that has turned into an incubus for me. (Her voice rises)
The thorn in women's flesh, the messenger from Satan sent to torment women is men and their technique is marriage.
I have decided to quit this hag-ridden life, (moves towards him, now furiously) without connubial happiness.
Without conjugal affection, without the pleasure which consummates life.
I've accumulated enough money and can afford my own home. I can take care of myself and I'll be in clover for ever. With his influence I have secured the job of the health officer in-charge of a comprehensive health centre.

With my money and status, I do not need any husband. Done with all he-men. I'm going to be free, as free as the air. The sky is my first step.

(*Opens the bedroom door, shows him the way out, as she points*)

THE ENTRANT (walks towards the door, prophetically):
-Madam! You will rue this day of your rash action. Marriage is the spice of every woman's life. And man is the rock on which a woman stands on this earth. Her rock of freedom.

Divorce is like the separation of humans from their maker, only at grave consequences. Divorce is like disconnection from your maker, your natural environment. It only results in death.

Divorce is like humankind gaining freedom from the spirit-kind at great peril. Women can only be free from men at their own peril because women have been made to be dependent on men, to showcase humans' dependency on their maker.

ROSE (stifles a laugh, almost shouting, fluidly):
-I will prove men wrong! I will prove Fate wrong! I will prove wrong the fallacy of dependency, that humankind must depend on the spirit-kind and, as its model, that women must depend on men.

I will prove that women can do without men and can survive outside marriage. I will prove providence, man, marriage and dependency, all combined wrong.

THE ENTRANT:
-The spiritual forces, working together for the purpose of preserving the reformed and destroying the deformed,

and the Highest being divine and supreme, can not be wrong.

ROSE:
The power of the gods symbolized as the superiority of men over women are worthless myths.

THE ENTRANT:
-Humanity cannot contest against Divinity. The creature cannot contend with her creator. The weak cannot oppose the strongest.

ROSE:
-I will confute the gods. Men will be confounded by their dispensability. Marriage, the trap that holds women in slavery will become old fashioned as women will prefer their freedom to the slavery of marriage. I will prove that a new order is possible. I've tasted beyond the gilt of gingerbread and taken the gloss of desirability off marriage. The die is cast. I must swop horses ere midstream. (*Stares at him wildly. Knocks on the opened door as she talks, in a non-negotiable manner*)

This day, I have taken this plunge, to be a divorcee, live in celibacy, embrace absolute freedom.
But it is with this resolution: to go all out with all the resources at my disposal, to teach these emotionless men,

(*Out of fear, the entrant steps out of the house*)

the lessons of their lives till they'll rue their heartlessness. I will sit on their heads till they buckle under me. For the 'corper' doctor sent to work under me, I shall sit on his head, knuckle his limbs and wring his neck until he shall regret his birth as a man.

THE ENTRANT (on the veranda, just by the door, again, prophetically):
-The loss of the cocoon that protects wives is DIVORCE. It symbolizes the fall of man from the pinnacle of his dominion, it is to remind and warn humans of the consequences of the fall of man from the rock of his protection, and to instruct humans that it usually culminates in death. As Humans can't be absolutely free from the spirit-kind, so is its paradigm, women can't be absolutely free from men because the same unseen strings that tie humans to the apron of the spirit-kind tie women to men.

ROSE (slams the door shut angrily, to his face, testily):
-Men (prodded by Fate) have bitten my nose, mindless of my catarrh. I will, in retaliation, bite their anus mind-less of the excrement thereof. I will sever the strings that tie humans to the apron of the gods, loosen men from the shackles of entrapment of the gods. I will disable the remote-controller with which the spirit-kind rule in the affairs of humans. I will set men free from the gods. I am self-comissioned to free the captives of the gods.

THE ENTRANT:
-You have not learnt from the response to command by the rising sun, cannot interpret the obedience of the setting Sun, investigate the disappearance of the shooting star or dicern the mystery of the dancing moon nor figure out the connection between the powers of the tongue of the spirit-kind and signs and wonders:
Because the gods cursed womanity, it is difficult to get a husband, marriage and motherhood are not for all women, and unless a woman is under her husband, she will be open to indiscriminate exploitation by all men, indicating that you cannot escape the consequences of

your actions and, unless humans are protected by God, they will be destroyed by the Devil, all surreptitiously orchestrated to establish that Humanity is in the hand of Divinity.

And all the things you behold under the firmament and hear happening around the universe and see beyond the figment of the firmament of the final Fantasy are to make Humankind to be in subjection to and live in awe of the spirit-kind.

Curtain falls.

ACT THREE. SCENE TWO

Concerning fatherhood: bride price father, foster, legal, deadbeat or acknowledged father are all fathers but only the DNA father is provable as authentic father, substantiating the fact that besides all the gods, there is only one true God with overriding power.

A SCENE IN THE ASO'S HOME
An artistically and luxuriously furnished apartment, happiness echoes from all the walls of the home. Contentment reflects on all the faces seen here. OBONG sits at his piano, while his father coaches him.

LANRE (instructively):
- 'Old boy', when you press this red button, the musical note obtained is 'Tenor' (OBONG presses the button).

When you press the purple button, you have the tone called 'Alto'. If you touch the blue button, the pitch obtained is the 'Contralto' (OBONG touches the button).
The brown button is for the 'Treble' chord while the black one is for 'Bass'.

OBONG (illustratively):
-Daddy, I also noticed yesterday that, when I touched the red and the purple buttons together, the tone I had was different.

So, I decided to call it 'Trenalto'. Today again, I pressed the brown and the black buttons at the same time and heard a new and entirely different tone altogether. What shall we call this new tone?

LANRE (impressed):
-You can call it 'Trebase'. That is creativity which you are abundantly endowed with. Tap it, as it comes to you. Now, enough with the piano. Take up your guitar and rehearse the song you composed.

(*OBONG, obediently, picks up the guitar and starts his new song, demonstrates with matching dance steps*)

Children, have you heard the news? Our nation is morally bankrupt and in debt. Our treasury is empty. Our leaders are the looters.
Their means is corruption and mismanagement. Our problem is our Leadership. Oh! What bad news!
Leaders of tomorrow, rise up and lead your people.
(To his father) Daddy, we must record and release this song soon.

RHAHAAB (standing directly behind them, and unseen by husband and son, interrupts):
-He is a very intelligent child. He only started learning this yesterday and is now singing so well.

LANRE (as both lift up their eyes to see her)
-I've noticed that too. That is why I'm unrelenting in my efforts at coaching him.

RHAHAAB (lovingly):
-Enough for today. Father and son, your table is ready, your food is begging for attention.
You have been rehearsing that song for three hours now, won't you eat tonight?

OBONG:
-Mummy, you may start eating, we will join you after rehearsing the next song (Sings).

There is no justice in this system. You have no other country than this one. So, where will you run to? Children, unite and defend your country.

Curtain falls

ACT THREE. SCENE THREE

Men's taste of their own pill

A SCENE IN ROSE'S OFFICE IN THE HOSPITAL
Morning. The office of the principal health officer in-charge is decorated artistically with expensive furniture and flowers. Faint music is heard from a small set on a high-quality desk, behind which sits Rose clad in the most expensive wears of the most current fashion. Rose is writing confidently at her desk and appears contented and on top of the world. The doctor, a young handsome man in ward-overall, sits with a long face on a stool opposite Rose. The scenery of the hospital outside the office sharply contrasts this picture. We see dilapidated buildings and unhappy labourers clad in clothes turn to shreds carrying buckets, brooms, and cutlasses cleaning the compound. Nurses in uniform briskly walk between these buildings.
She stops writing, lowers the music, and looks contemptuously at the doctor.

ROSE (all are seated, facing her suspiciously):
-Doctor, we have noticed that you've stopped seeing patients. So, I called my senior staff, along with myself here. We will give you our ears to hear your own story. Maybe you have reasons for your action, or inaction, which is unbecoming of a person who attends to the sick.

DOCTOR (plaintively):
-I am drawing your attention to certain anomalies in the management of this Health Centre, which is not in the interest and welfare of patients and myself.

Till a stop is put to these unfortunate happenings, I shall stop pretending to be looking after the welfare of the patients.

THE HOSPITAL SECRETARY (interrupts):
-In the centre we have the nurses, the Community Health Officers and the other Junior Staff. You are the only doctor here. (Sits down, calmy)
You see all patients, admit, treat and discharge them, while the Health Officer in-charge of the centre oversees the other aspects of management of the hospital.
You should not see this arrangement as having two captains in one ship.
The two of you should work hand in hand. If you have any suggestions as to how we all could work together to improve the overall care given to the patients, kindly let us know: that is why we called this meeting.

ROSE (conceitedly):
-We have only thirty minutes for this meeting. Let him just voice out his grievances. We are already hung unto his lips.

DOCTOR (peremptorily):
-The Health Officer in-charge, you have been using the hospital's ambulance as your private car; even spending several weekends in your hometown with the ambulance while critically ill patients die here because there is no vehicle to convey them to the General Hospital, where there are better facilities for treating them.

Secondly, you sometimes force patients to buy fuel for the ambulance's use before it can convey them to the General Hospital. You also instructed labourers to use buckets they also use in washing patient's toilets to fetch water for me.

I implored you to repair the chairs in my house, but till today, there is nothing for me to sit on. In spite of my asking you urgently and repeatedly, you have refused to repair the refrigerator and kerosene stove for use in my house and the hospital.

ROSE (interrupts as she swings round and round in her swivel-chair portraying her position as the be-all and the end-all. She points to the doctor as her underdog. Haughtily):
-You must realise that you are an N.Y.S.C.[7] member, and N.Y.S.C. means: 'Now your suffering continues.' You must be apprised that this is your year of mandatory suffering.

As a common 'corper', you have no business telling me, the officer-in-charge of the hospital, how I should use the ambulance or manage the hospital.

Supplying water to a 'corper' is a privilege, not a right, and since you do not appreciate this, that gesture is stopped forth with, you must fetch your water yourself. And if I may ask you, how many 'corpers' in the country enjoy the facility of refrigeration? Other 'corpers' work in the farms, dig gutters along our roads, while you are here, soliciting for comfort. Now your suffering continues, corper. I declare this unnecessary meeting ended.

(*Everybody in the meeting place except Rose gets going. The Secretary scurries to meet the Doctor outside the office, hopelessly*)

---

[7] NYSC stands for: National Youth Service Corps – a one-year compulsory service for Nigerian graduates.

THE SECRETARY (in a whisper):
-Beware, sir, beware of divorcees! They are beings once maltreated by men, since then vengeful on other men. They are like the proud old Lucifer, the Serpent condemned to hell fire, conscious of his inescapable fate, avowedly persecuting God's followers.

They are like the former heavenly tenant, just because he has been evicted, he will not allow humans to enter heaven.

They are like the scorpion, with a venomed mind and a poisonous tail.

(*Both get going, slowly*)

The rabid dog with an infected brain barks and bites indiscriminately. So do divorcees, with inflamed minds and sore feelings. They vent their spleen on other people. Beware of divorcees! They are deadly! They are malicious! They are fiend incarnates!

DOCTOR (astonished):
-Is she a divorcee?

THE SECRETARY (mockingly):
-She was married with children, but bad character evicted her from her matrimonial home.

DOCTOR:
-No wonder she does all these things!

THE SECRETARY:
-You haven't known what havoc she has wreaked on men. The bit you've known is the tip of the iceberg. The hospital's labourers fetch water for her, sweep her house, wash her panties and do her chores every day.

In fact, these men at her beck and call wait on her hand and foot. The exploited men were once so bitter that they unanimously decided on a service revolt to throw off their yoke of servitude.

With one mind they went to her and said, 'We are employed by the government, paid by the government to work for the public or at worst to be servile to the government, but not to an individual.

The pompous officer bragged to her servitors: 'As a government official, I am entitled to government cooks, stewards and labourers.' And she gave them all queries. The intimidated men, without any option, continue in their thraldom and have ever since not complained anymore.

She does nothing with the imprest money she collects monthly for the supply of daily requirements in the hospital.

Everything we request for use in the hospital, she writes back in the requisition book: 'Out of stock'.

DOCTOR:
-Why has she not been reported to the Ministry?

THE SECRETARY:
-Report? getting there from here is very costly. And even when you get there, the messenger will ask for bribe before being able to submit your petitions to the senior officers, who will not do anything since they are birds of a feather. Like kettle and pot, both are black, so black that like people living in glass houses they dare not throw stones, lest their houses break and expose them to the open.

DOCTOR:

-The problem with this country is that those at the top are so insulated that their underlings cannot check their excesses. They are on top, oppressive selfish and do what they like. Those above them cannot bring them under control because they are not beyond reproach as well and their underdogs have no provisions for getting their wrongs redressed.

Curtain falls.

ACT THREE. SCENE FOUR

Blood is thicker than water

A SCENE IN EBONG'S HOUSE: a five star home with a glamorous setting. In this high-brow area is sitting a duplex. Success radiates from all the walls of the apartment but quietness is pervasive. There are no children playing or in sight here - creating as still as a mouse situation. Ebong returns from work, enters his house, turns on the television, sits on a sofa, watches the television as he unfastens his buttons and unknots his tie and loosens his shoelaces.

MUSICAL VIDEO FROM THE TELEVISION:
Children, have you heard the news?
Our nation is morally bankrupt and in debt.
Our treasury's completely empty.
Our Leaders are the looters.
Their means is corruption and mismanagement.
Our problem is bad leadership.
Freedom from colonial masters
into Corruption by African looters.
Out of the frying pan into the fire
Oh! What bad news!

Leaders of tomorrow, rise up and lead your people.
Our future's as bleak as a church rat's.
Bad leadership has destroyed our nation.
Oh! What a pitiable situation!
Liberation from slave masters into
Mismanagement by African leaders.
From fry pan to fire.
Leaders of tomorrow, rise up and lead your country.

(With exaggerated theatrics that portray the young musician, as doing beyond his age)

Our Leaders trot abroad for periodic medical check-ups. Whilst kwashiorkor is phasing us out at home. Their slogan is: Death to the children, long life to the aged. Their mantra is: for me, my family and peers but nothing for the masses.

The rising generation, arise and fight for your lives.

Their children school and holiday in Zurich. While we, under ramshackle roofs, pay for substandard education. Oh! What a disparity! Children, rise up and fight for your rights.

(The young star displays incredible dance steps that matches the rhythm of the music)

There is no justice in this system. You have no other country than this one. So, where will you run to?
"A luta continua, Vitoria e certa"
Children, unite and defend your country.

 EBONG (with the music still in the background):
 -This is a rare talent. He has tremendous charisma and stage presence. Young, but ahead of his time.

MUSICAL VIDEO FROM THE TELEVISION:
Their children's lot is a guaranteed life of plenty.
Ours's that of hunger, starvation and deprivation.
Oh! How discriminatory is Fate? The struggle continues, victory is certain.
Babes and suckling, arise and fight for your country.

(The performance of the young screen idol is electrifying)

214

There is no justice in this system, with foreign debts hanging on our neck, terrorism, kidnapping, violence decimating us; fraud becoming our religion, our system without justice; unemployment suffocating us, hunger and starvation staring at our faces; millions of our children out of school, sickness and diseases discomforting us; hopelessness our lingua franca, our future's as bleak as a church rat's, where the winner takes all and only the fittest survives. Children, unite and fight for justice.
Emancipate yourselves from corruption and mismanagement. Emancipate yourselves from "monkey de work, baboon de chop". Break away from the pauperization of the masses because the power in the masses is greater than the power of the leaders.

EBONG (thoughtfully):
-This is a gifted child; he has set the Thames on fire.

SOUND FROM THE TELEVISION:
The music you are listening to, which has been in the first position of the top ten chart for ten consecutive months, is the masterpiece of little master OBONG, the seven-year-old youngest megastar whose debut album won him the international award for the world's best musician for the year, the international award for the bestselling record in the world.

And a cash price of one million dollars for the youngest entertainer in the world. The music star is the son of Mister Lanre Aso and Mrs. Rhahaab Aso.

EBONG (stares unbelievably at the young star on the screen, reflectively):
-This young star is the facsimile of my great grandfather.

The teeth gap in his mouth, the hair line, the starry eyes, the slender build, the polished complexion and the 'bossing' temple are the gifts of the chip of the old block from the old, old block.

And his mother, former Miss Rhahaab, was my girl-friend of five uninterrupted years. That friendship, which ended with pregnancy, has this young boy as its fall out.

(Stares musingly at the boy on the screen) This star is mine, my own blood. I must claim my child at all costs.

My blood is mine forever.

Curtain falls.

ACT THREE. SCENE FIVE

Blood bond

A SCENE IN THE SCHOOL
During recess, in a five-star school, all the children are playing outside in the field. EBONG fishes OBONG out of a group of children at play, carries him high up in the air, hugs him and puts him down on the ground

EBONG (dotingly):
-How are you?

OBONG (short of words, looks at him in a strange manner, sharply):
-Fine, thank you.

EBONG (fondly):
-I am your father.

OBONG (startled):
-Daddy?

EBONG:
-Yes, I am your daddy. Take this sweet, take this chin-chin, take this pen and pencil.
(Hands over items to him, fatherly)

OBONG (hesitates, then receives the items):
-Thank you.

EBONG (hugs him again winingly):
-Just as I visited you last week, I will see you again next week.

(Obong nods happily)

217

(*Exits*)

(*OBONG calls his playmates and distributes sweets and chin-chin to them*)

FIRST PLAYMATE (happily):
-A-ah, sweets, meat-pie and chin-chin.

SECOND PLAYMATE (peeps into OBONG'S pocket, prattles):
-And also pen and pencil. Who gave them to you? My daddy said I should not accept gifts from strangers because the strangers may be ghosts.

OBONG (defends his actions, babbles):
-He is not a ghost. He said he is my father.

THIRD PLAYMATE (collects the sweets, inquisitively):
-The one who usually picks you home after school or the one who came last week?

OBONG (explains further):
-The one who came last week and gave me money for akara. He has just left.

FOURTH PLAYMATE (munching away at a hard chin-chin, pryingly, prates):
-How many fathers do you have?

OBONG (gabbles):
-I don't know o-oh! Maybe they are many.

FIRST PLAYMATE (licking the sweets, tattles):
-Me, I have only one father.

THIRD PLAYMATE (crunching a hard chin-chin, twiddles):

-And me too! I have only one father. My daddy usually buys things for me.

SECOND PLAYMATE:

-I have only one father and he loves me very much.

FOURTH PLAYMATE (prattles):

-Me, I have no father.

FIRST PLAYMATE:

-Why? Is your father dead?

FOURTH PLAYMATE (prates):

-No! I have never had a father at all.

THIRD PLAYMATE (concernedly):

-Did you ask your mummy about your father?

FOURTH PLAYMATE:

-Yes! She said I must never ask such questions again.

OBONG (educates them):

-My mummy said everybody has a father, since no child has ever, like the soya beans seed, fallen from its pod unto this earth. Nor has any man before fallen from the moon unto this earth. So, she said, 'No child is fatherless'. You must have a father.

FIRST PLAYMATE:

-No! He is a bastard!

SECOND PLAYMATE:

-Who is a bastard?

FIRST PLAYMATE:
-A fatherless child.

THIRD PLAYMATE:
- My mother said they are hapless public children, without identity; sans sac and soc

SECOND PLAYMATE:
- My Mummy said they are the unclaimed, alien children that stray into our world, without toll and team.

THIRD PLAYMATE:
- My mom said they are the ' born-throw-aways', without help and hope, like the Queen's first grand son who was born with curses of bastardy, spiritual handicap, social stigma; he is rejected, deserted, without links with his ancestry or disconnected from his true roots; ridiculed, dejected and living in a void with a false identity - all, baggage he carries and hurdles he must overcome.

SECOND PLAYMATE:
-My mother said they are hapless......

OBONG:
-You mean the one with the birth-right of the first-born son in a royal family who is supposed to inherit his father's possessions and authority? My mum said he is the rightful heir to the throne, who now is denied sonship because his father denied being his father and by extension his family, then his country denied him citizenship - chains of non-acceptance and loss of heritage just because of the father's rejection of his duty of fathership. He is now eaten up by the agony of uncertainty of his true father's identity and is floating like an abandoned vessel in the ocean with his heart pierced by the arrow of

bastardy - my mother never ceases to warn against the curses of bastardy.

FIRSTPLAYMATE:

-He was conceived in sin, begotten out of wedlock, not a product of mistake but an unintended outcome of an intentional action, like the side-effect of a drug deliberately taken for its curative effect; he was born as an illegitimate child and so disowned - these circumstances robbed him of the right to be the future king, the right to be a son or family member or a citizen or guidance by his ancestors - those were what my mother said were the curses of bastardy , the punishment for the disobedience of parents visited on the products of their sinful actions.

SECOND PLAYMATE:

-The parents ate sour grape, the child's teeth is set on edge even when the covenant of Grace has replaced the covenant of sacrifice, my mother preaches repeatedly.

Did the bastard, the product of parental sin choose how he was conceived or begotten? Why are some children rejected by their fathers and some are not?

FIRST PLAYMATE:

-Luck! Pure luck.

All fingers are not equal, so are all children not equally lucky. Some are conceived in sin, claimed by their fathers, some, not so lucky, are not, different strokes for different folks; same Grace upon all, but different fates, heaven and hell, as prepared, await different folks, different statuses for different children, so my mummy said. Some humans will go to heaven, some to hell; some women will marry and some will not; some children will have fathers but some will be fatherless, the Lord God,

221

who made them all, made it so - that is the song 🎵 I grew up to hear my mummy sing.

OBONG:
-He did not eat the sour grape with his parents nor choose his parents or the circumstances of his birth, neither chose he to be rejected and should not be made to suffer for circumstances foisted on him.

THIRD PLAYMATE:
-Such is life. My Mummy said we are not the architect of our fates but the gods who make us who we are or what we turn out to be. They determine how we are conceived, whether or not we are claimed and our statuses.

OBONG:
-The bastards and the legitimate children are potential contributors to the society - acceptance or rejection of fatherhood by their fathers regardless, the curses of bastardy are unfair. The circumstances of our birth, the colour of our skin, how we are conceived, where we are born or die, like the gift of life are beyond human control. They are assigned to us by the gods and should not be a cause of pain for anyone or weapons of oppression and discrimination against anyone - my mummy once said.

FIRST PLAYMATE:
-They are unclaimed......

THIRD PLAYMATE:
-They are born throwaway.......

FIRST PLAYMATE:
-.......It is not the fault.....end in Heaven or in Hell

222

SECOND PALYMATE (jeeringly, to fourth play-mate):
-Bastard, leave our company.

OBONG (defensively):
-Why? Leave him alone. No one is fatherless.

SECOND PALYMATE (pushes the fourth playmate away, blathers):
-No! my mummy said I should never keep company with children from broken homes, lest they spoil me.

THIRD PLAYMATE (childishly):
-No! He is not from a broken home. I know their house, a white building. It is not broken.

SECOND PLAYMATE (taunting and still pushing the fourth playmate away. Matter-of-factly):
-But he is homeless.

THIRD PLAYMATE (candidly):
-No! He has a home. I know their house. He lives in a white house with his mummy.

SECOND PLAYMATE (gives the fourth playmate a shove. Frankly):
-Mummy alone does not make a home. 'Mummy, daddy and children make a home': so my mummy said.

(*The fourth playmate cries as he walks away. He was the scoff of the other children, except OBONG*)

SECOND PLAYMATE (crackles, to others):
-You must not keep company with such children. They will make you become a bad child, like them.

FIRST PLAYMATE (points in the direction of an approaching adult):
-His second father is coming.
(Crackles, then to others) Let's go. Leads.

(*All except OBONG exeunt*)

LANRE (parks near where they were standing):
-Old boy? Who gave you all those things?

OBONG (gives no reply)

LANRE (stammers):
-Throw everything away. Never accept gifts from strangers.
(OBONG complies)
Take this meat pie for your brunch. Mummy will come to pick you home after school: be a good boy.

OBONG (thoughtfully):
-Daddy, why is it that some children have daddies and others do not?

LANRE (Surprised):
-The Lord God made them so.

OBONG:
-Why has God made them so; given some children father but not others?

LANRE:
-That is what pleases God.

OBONG:
-So, he is happy that some children have no father?

LANRE:

-So that he will have the opportunity to be father to those children without father.

OBONG:

-So, God did not give my classmate a father so that he can take the place of his father? He wants to be a father too? He is a Jealous God.

LANRE:

-He is the father of all of us. Eat your meat pie and don't ask such questions again.

(Obong is now more confused. He eats his meat- pie, slowly.)

OBONG:
-Thank you, Daddy.

Curtain falls.

ACT THREE. SCENE SIX

Human-life is coordinated by rival unseen forces. A bi-facedness: one deforms and devours, the other forewarns of the omen, reforms and preserves; instantiated by the violator that savages, ravages or defiles and the husband that feasts on, then sanctifies a woman.

A SCENE IN ROSE'S HOME
A staff nurse on her way to Rose's house, bemusedly

STAFF NURSE (soliloquizing):
-This bitch, what wrong have I done her again? Like a witch has she been persecuting me. Spitefully, like the little house rat which bites off the sole of one's feet and soothes the irritating wound with spittle does she, with a bewitching smile on her seemingly innocent face and a bedevilled mind punish me.

Often times, for minor offences like my not putting on the nurses' shoes or belt she gives me severe punishment. How many times have I not been the target of her misplaced aggression? Sometimes, in a fit of spleen she vents her frustration on me.

How many times has this hag victimized me these few years for no reasons at all. And that is in spite of my, as a sop thrown to Cerberus, precautionary observance of all rules in my working place. In sooth, I am a victim of this vermin's displaced spite.

These divorcees, their ill-will to their ex-husbands always spills over to other people, especially their married counterparts. Envy usually festers in their minds. That is why she has been making things warm for me.

(Stops talking as she gets to Rose's house. Knocks and waits until the door opens)

ROSE (happily, as if she was prepared and expecting to match her, fire for fire):
  -Staff, you are here!

STAFF NURSE (looks cross-eyed at her):
  -Yes! 'In-charge', I have answered the query you gave me. Now, you said I must do night-duty for one week as punishment. What is my offence?

ROSE (blustering):
  -You reported to your new station without obtaining discharge letter and clearance from me.

STAFF NURSE (still looking daggers at her):
  -I told you that my husband came to pack my things to my new station, and I seized that opportunity to kill two birds with one stone, used his car as free transport to my new station.
  That was after we collected my transfer letter from the Ministry.

ROSE (more infuriated, emphatically):
  -That is why you must be punished.

STAFF NURSE (petrified, spontaneously):
  -Because of my husband?

ROSE (authoritatively):
  -Yes!

STAFF NURSE (curiously):
  -Just because of my husband?

228

ROSE (speculatively):
-Your husband is supposed to know civil service rules.

STAFF NURSE (convinced):
-So, you are jealous?

ROSE (dismissively):
-Jealous of what? Are you insulting me?

STAFF NURSE (audaciously):
-Jealous of my being a wife! Envious that I have a husband. Begrudging my Mrs tittle, my prize, my crown. You are resentful of my portfolio: exclusive service to my king, not being indiscriminately defiled by all and sundry, my 'wifery' office, my place of rest, your desideratum, that accords me honour and reverence. Whom the gods choose to destroy, they first punish by taking rest away from and then make them run from pillar to post. The gods are angry with you - that is why you are being tossed from one man's prick to the other. As you refuse to submit to one man, you must submit to sundry men, and rest and peace must elude you - the law of nature is that you must worship something. The war in the spiritual and physical realms is about exclusive service and submission.

ROSE (now understands her, resentfully):
-Pish! Get away from here, go and do your one week-night-duty before I can give you discharge letter to your new station.

STAFF NURSE (spitefully):
-You are jealous of my having a husband. Better go and look for one instead of victimizing those who have

husbands; otherwise, the torments of jealousy will make you go mad.

ROSE (maliciously):
-If you insult me again, I will increase your night-duty to two weeks.

STAFF NURSE (angrily):
-Increase my punishment to one year night-duty, provided you will not steal my husband. I am aware of your failed attempts at snatching people's husbands. Go to auction market and buy a husband instead of stealing one.

ROSE (retorts, angrily):
-Did I tell you that I need a husband?

STAFF NURSE (as if she is educating a novice):
-Pretenders do the worst. Don't pretend. As humans' hunger for food and thirst for water, so do women crave for men. Every woman needs a man.
I saw the way you were seducing my husband with your squinty eyes the other day. If I was not there you would have cast your spell on him. Your wizardry will not work on me. Try elsewhere.

ROSE (disdainfully):
-That ugly poor man of yours? Do you still classify such as a husband?

STAFF NURSE:
-Which type do you have? Even if you buy or steal a husband, can your bad character enable you to keep a husband? Your type cannot maintain a man. Husband is not 'Moi moi' (beans pudding).
Marriage is not for your type. Husband is not for every woman. The gods have hardened your heart such that

your type cannot submit to a man - the gods have barred your type from marriage. As your pastor told you: Flawed character is the albatross round your neck, the demon lurking within and self-sabotaging you and your Destiny destroyer. Penance, position, power, piety and charity will not buy you a husband nor give you rest and peace of mind.

It is not the destiny's fault if you do not have a husband, not because of the demon monitoring you, not because of the enemy's actions but it is the outcome of your wicked character: vengefulness. Like other divorcees, because men used you without compensation, you are seething with bitterness. Vengeance is your religion, unfortunately directed against innocent soft targets.

So, if you want to marry, follow the advice of the Dutch: as you deposit money into your bank, also deposit good character into your bankrupt soul and change your behaviour, otherwise you will live alone and die alone. Men will only use, destroy and dump you. Your type is only good for use, not for keeps. You are not marriageable; you are not manageable. You are mad. It is only a foolish woman that will say she does not need a husband.

You are foolish, like the poor man that will prefer his thatched house to a zinc-roofed house because it is hot unlike his thatched house. Poor in mind, poor in cash and poor in kindness. You are, in addition, poor in character and you will die in loneliness. Women who are slated for destruction by the gods are first tossed from one man to the other.

(Rose listens on in subjection to her taunts. Staff nurse goes out, while Rose angrily slams the swinging door shut behind the staff nurse. Rose moves into her bedroom. Dejectedly, with her eyes bedimmed with tears)

ROSE (gloomily):
-What awkward predicament is this? Rose?

(*Looks into the mirror and fixes a gaze on her image in the mirror*)

Is this that same acme of beauty? In tens did they come; prowling, wooing, begging that once-upon-a-time Queen of beauty. Then they petered out.

Next, the comers were only fun seekers. Left with those only fond of fun, I started hunting, I hunted, hunted and hunted. Bereft of hope for what my heart craved for, I entered into an association (looks at her image again in the mirror) which was a mockery of marriage.

That mock marriage, unrecognized by the society, was what I, for the sake of peace of mind, opted out of. Out I was! Here I am, single! Single! Single!

(*Backs away from the mirror, slowly towards the bed*)

Now I am free, I've got money and I've attained heights. Singleness, freedom, money, high status: what do they mean to me? Wretched pelf dogged by damnation!

Pelf that cannot buy happiness, nor can it save me from insults.

(*Sits on the bed, carries a pillow on her head*)

Heights that cannot command respect, nor are they impervious to sarcastic gibes; singleness, that is a subject of jibes, without satisfaction above all, remains the same flesh, still desirous of companionship; freedom into mental agony: all are like the piece of bone a child throws to the dog or barrenness of the highest order.

(Lies on the bed as the pillow falls on her chest)

Now, I am left bereft by this predicament.

Last week, a young girl challenged me to produce a husband and prove to the world that I have that magic charm, the lure every woman uses to attract and own a man.

Last month, I was to be given a chieftaincy tittle for excelling over all my compeers. At the dying minute, one of the king makers humorously remarked: 'Can an unmarried woman, a divorcee, be made a chief?'. Like a slip between the cup and the lips, this vanity of freedom wrestled that crown off my head, so did the covetous role of matron of Girls' Guide and patroness of Youth Movement slip me by.

The instigated youths who first approached me for these roles gave as reason for their change of mind: these are roles that call for perfect marriage as a quintessence to the youths.

Yesterday a girl called me 'an old maid (walks to the door with the pillow held close to her chest) whom nobody would want as a wife.

Today, insults, everyday insults, fits of the mopes. This my dreary life is, remote controlled by the gods, like that of a bear baited with dogs. Like a bear chained to a stake, and tormented by a pack of grey hounds, I am stuck in this cleft stick and hounded every passing second by the cruel, sneering and insulting remarks of all and sundry, the haves and even the have-nots, the offscourings of humanity.

(Throws the pillow on to the bed)

That is my portion, the allotment of a divorcee, the garment of shame, the price of absolute freedom.

(Hears a knock on the door and the hoarse voice of a man with flip flops slapping sounds as he shuffles noisily. Hurries to the door and opens)

ROSE (angrily):
-Yes! What can I do for you?

VISITOR (yawns):
-Let, let us go inside.

ROSE (pointedly):
-Look at this swarm of flies following you about because of the stench of wine on you. Are you drunk?

VISITOR (lurches, obviously inebriated):
-Eh! Drink is drunk.

ROSE (repulsed by the miasma of stale alcohol emanating from him, advisedly):
-Then go home and sleep.

VISITOR (staggers and belches, drunkenly):
-That is why, that is why, I am here to ejaculate.

ROSE:
-You are here to do what? If you are drunk, go home and sleep.

VISITOR (still swaggering and belching):
-No! When drinkie is full, I call here to drop.

ROSE (stigmatised):
-Call here to do what?

VISITOR (prates sottishly):
-When any man is full, and fullness is tense, drink comes here to empty.

ROSE:
-Why?

VISITOR:
-Are you not a woman?

ROSE:
-I am a woman. And so?

VISITOR:
-Every woman is a treadmill on which men do exercises to relieve tension. A grinding stone upon which the seeds are squeezed onto. A receptacle for men's effusion. A temple for recreation, procreation and accommodation.

ROSE (cuts him short...):
-Really, every woman is a treadmill on which men exercise to ease tension? Grinding stone? Receptacle? All those glowing and flowery adjectives? For every woman? Including your mother and Grandma?

VISITOR (as if his eyes are clear now, in quick succession, scrutinizingly):
-Are you married? Do you have a husband? Are you not a single woman?

ROSE (inquisitively):
-What is the difference between a single and a married woman?

VISITOR:
-A married woman is a no-go area. A single woman is an all-comer's free land. I thought you were a harlot.

ROSE:

-What does a harlot do that a married woman does not do?

VISITOR:

-One does with one man only. One does with all men.

ROSE:

-So, both do the same thing, serve the same purpose. They are not different then.

(*Slams the door shut in his face and runs inside, weeping*)

VISITOR:

-Ah! Aha! There are different types of women.

(*Belches, almost vomits and staggers along, makes his way out as smells of vomit wafts from his mouth*)
Woman, you don't want me? Jezebel, I thought you were a prostitute. Every single woman is. You are! Free for all men. Woman! You don't want me, why?
Free women are free for all men, let me go.

(*Wobbles as he walks away, kicking stones from one sidewalk to the other*)

(*ROSE cries loudly from her bedroom, with face bedewed with hot glistening tears*)

ROSE (in a state of great mental distress, in a lamenting manner):

-Oh! All ye women! May no other girl go through these hoops! This war in my heart, this pain in my mind, this fire on my head, this gnawing agony, this anguish without any salve. May I be the sacrificial lamb to the gods. May this my condign cross appease the angry gods.

(*The telephone rings*)

May my experience on this rack to the ears of all girls be a lesson which shall save them

(*She ignores the repeatedly ringing telephone, walks about confusedly*)

from this racking experiences. May the story of my ignominious single status, like the stench of rotting fish that attracts sundry flies save them from this ignoble unmarried fate. Girls! Know this! All men see unmarried women as towels for general use, as public toilets where every full Jack can open up.

Every day, they harass me, Jackasses, working colleagues, drunkards, all and one (sinks down into a chair beside a dog); men see me as their object of self-gratification.

To be free from this humiliation, harassment and violations, for these reasons I have today decided: I will use my position, my money, all at my disposal (strokes the dog lovingly) to buy a man who will serve me, at least as a dog, in driving away all these unwanted men.

My generation, note this: the animal that escapes from a trap avoids every semblance of a trap because it has learnt the hard way. So, should my experience on this rack be a lesson to prompt women to seek protection under a man; and as a model, to teach humans to seek protection under the creator.

The spirit-kind orchestrates these my experiences in campaigns to make me alignable or bring me into conformity with the ethos of the place that has been prepared for me (marriage) or for humans to learn from and be goaded to their assigned destination (heaven).

I am merely an actress, the world my stage, my life a mere drama, scripted, staged and directed by Providence - my assigned role remotely orchestrated; I am tossed and turned, spun around throughout life, as they enter, take over, act in us and through us, then cast us to demonstrate and prove that: because a woman is sweet like the nectar that attracts sipping bees, unless she is protected by a husband she will be indiscriminately sampled and violated by sundry men; and to convince humans that because they are like rotten fishes whose stench attracts sundry pecking flies, unless they are protected by their creator they will be similarly poked until devoured by the devil; and so are all human lives - tele-guided drama, cloaked and hooded human lives, voices and handwriting of humans, but scripted by the single purposed driven but bi-faced spirit-kind, cast to draw out lessons to fore-warn, lead or mislead humans to the places prepared for them.

The wife and the concubine live with the same man and serve the same purpose, but at different levels, the baboon is ground dwelling and the monkey is a tree-top dweller, but are both monkeys, so do the two facets of the spirit-kind lead by persuasion and subterfuge or mislead by luring humans to their assigned destinations. Unity of purpose in duplexity of forms.

Purpose: to take humans to the assigned destination. I am cast to serve as forewarning concerning your tour guide.

On our own, without this forewarning (Grace that is sufficient), we perish. You are warned by the story of my life so you will not perish.

Curtains fall.

ACT THREE. SCENE SEVEN

The sonship of God is a privilege that carries responsibilities, so is fathership, but like the corollary, you cannot have the privilege of harvest after shirking your responsibilities

A SCENE IN THE ASO'S FAMILY
Peace, happiness, contentment and fulfilment are pervasive in the atmosphere and written on everyone's face here.

RHAHAAB (cheerfully shouts, as she walks towards the dining table, hilariously):
-Father and son have finished eating. They left the grubby table for mother alone to clear, as if I'm their housemaid.
Come on! Obong, come and clear all these dirty plates you used.

LANRE (good- humouredly):
-Rha, please, leave 'old boy' alone. He is still too young to do the job of a housemaid.

RHAHAAB (Obong walks away from the dining table, believing that his father is supporting him):
-Who is too young? This old man who has recorded an album, won international awards and is a millionaire?
(Gives Obong a vigorous push) Come on: go and clear that table. Your father will make you lazy.
By sparing the rod, he is spoiling his child. Doesn't he know that saplings, (packs the plates for Obong) trees, while young with slender stems, are flexible and easily bent in any directions? But, beyond that stage, when the stem has grown sturdy, they are as stiff as iron rod.

So are children: while still in their swaddling clothe they are like hot iron rods: malleable. But once out of the swaddling clothe, unmoulded, they are like the bow of Odysseus: unbowed by all suitors.

LANRE (Gets up, light-heartedly):
-Darling, are you jealous of his millions? My son is still a baby. Leave my baby alone.

RHAHAAB (submissively):
-Male chauvinist, I know you don't think a male should do domestic chores. Then, seriously speaking, you must get me a house help.
I'm over working myself. After office work, I get cracking with housework. This is not the best for my health and is responsible for the life-expectancy of women being lower than that of the men.

LANRE (walks towards them, insistently):
-But that is the work of a wife.

RHAHAAB:
-And what is the work of the husband and the son? Eating food only?

LANRE (academically):
-Giving security and protection to the family.

RHAHAAB (sarcastically):
-Protection against armed robbers?

LANRE:
-At least, protection against the lustful ogling eyes of other men. A wife is fully insured and protected against indiscriminate attacks.

RHAHAAB (amused, then hilariously):
-But those eyes are not as harmful as the eyes of those young girls who make you come home late every day. My dear darling, when will you find me a house help?

LANRE (assuredly):
-I'll get you a good house girl tomorrow.

RHAHAAB (shakes her head, disapprovingly):
-No! No! No! I don't want a maid.

LANRE (with a cynical smile):
-Oh! You don't want a help anymore?

RHAHAAB (mockingly):
-I have told you, I want to handle a fish but not a fish as slippery as an eel. I want a water-animal, but not a toad whose croak is bad, but its venom is worse. I want a fish, but not an eel, that can set up electric shock that can pull off a great coup and overthrow me in my matrimonial home.

LANRE (pre-emptively):
-So, what then do you want?

RHAHAAB (amusingly):
-I want a house-boy.

LANRE (shouts, hoarsely):
-House –boy! Am I then the one who will like to be overthrown in my house?

(*Both laugh, infectiously*)

RHAHAAB (wipes her hands. From behind, she puts her hands round his neck, pushes him towards a settee):

-But darling, you know that I cannot condescend to such a level.

LANRE (affectionately):
-What makes you think I can stoop so low?

RHAHAAB (both sit down, congenially but disputatiously):
-Because when it comes to unbridled passions, men are worse than dogs: they are like 'Itong-ke-eto', the mushroom that grows on all trees mindless of sorts.

LANRE (waspishly):
-Women are just giving men bad names so that they may have reasons to shout: 'Crucify men!'.
The kettle knows that it wears a black coat of soot. But it doesn't want to give the pot the chance to say: 'as black as the coat of kettle'.
If we must have a house–help, we must have a 'good' house-girl and a house boy, so that if there will be any family coup d'etat, we will both be over–thrown.

(OBONG, who has completed clearing the table, joins them in the sitting room as a butterfly darts inside through the door which he kept open. OBONG shouts and upsets every furniture in the house as he tries to catch the butterfly)

RAHAHAAB (shouts, gratingly):
-Hei, Hei, Hei, don't turn this house upside down just because you want to catch a mere butterfly.

LANRE (harshly):
-E- eh, Mrs. Aso, treat him like an egg. Don't be hostile to him.

RHAHAAB (jovially):

-Oh! father, taking sides already with your son? So, I am the ownerless stray chicken. Because my father is not here to defend me. Alright. Son, pull down your father's house. He has money to build another one.

OBONG (tattles):

-Mummy, mummy, butterfly (points as he tries to catch it). Grandma said if a butterfly enters somebody's house, that is a sign that an important visitor is on the way to that house.

RHAHAAB (analytically):

-So, who are you expecting?

LANRE (sounding interested in the topic):

-Even myself, when I walked in today, I hit my left big toe against a stone. Our fathers believe that hitting the left toe like that is ominous of trouble or disaster while hitting the right toe is a good omen.

So, I can't figure out what is impending over us.

RHAHAAB (OBONG continues to chase the butterfly, anticipatorily):

-So, in spite of all your doses of education, you are still superstitious? Even though my left eyelid has been pulsating all-day-long, I don't care a tinker's cuss about it because I know it signifies nothing. Our people believe that such throbbing on the left side of the body is inauspicious.

Whereas it forebodes well if the throbbing is on the right. I dismiss all such baseless beliefs as ignorance and superstition.

LANRE (sounding academically):

-This life is deep, intricate and coordinated by unseen forces. First, the butterfly, then I kicked a stone and then your eye-lid started pulsating: surely, the gods are intimating us of an inauspicious moment to come.

The bi-facedness of the unseen forces is always at work: one prepares the slaughter slab, the other, like conscience, forewarns of the omen.

Since you reject and sell old ideas down the river on imbibing new ones, how do you explain these observations?

RHAHAAB:

-Well, my eyelid has been pulsating because my body directs blood flow there in response to some irritation.

LANRE:

-What about my hitting a stone?

RHAHAAB (OBONG stumbles and falls, still chasing the butterfly):

-You kicked a stone because you were not careful. If you were looking in your direction, you would have seen and avoided the stone.

LANRE (gets up, helps him to get up):

-But more often than not, throbbing of eyelids fore warns events. As the crowing of the cock is a harbinger of dawn and swallows the forerunners of spring, so is the visit of a butterfly a herald of visitors.

RHAHAAB (heuristically):

-Coincidence! That's why it's not invariably so, but coincidentally so. There are no scientific proofs for such beliefs.

LANRE (stands over her, the way a lecturer does his student, authoritatively):

-You talk of scientific proofs. Our forefathers came to those conclusions and made those deductions that have stood the racket after centuries of onerous observations.

Observation! Is that not the basis of science? Are these beliefs then not the product of science? How then do you explain the age-old observation of butterflies, the fore runners of visitors?

RHAHAAB (disagreeing):

-Things we do not understand or cannot explain, we tag "mysteries" and ascribe to the gods – including our carelessness and mental laziness. Well, that butterfly entered our house because Obong kept the door open. If the doors were closed, how would it have entered?

(*OBONG, on hearing that, goes to close the half-opened door. At the door, he sees an approaching visitor, takes a second look, recognizes the visitor. He runs out, shouting: 'daddy! daddy! daddy! daddy! daddy! daddy!' The visitor embraces OBONG, picks him up, throws him high up in the air, catches him at mid-air and holds him close to his bosom as he walks through the door into the sitting room, muttering tenderly*):

VISITOR (with approbation):

-Blood, my dear blood, my dear, blood, indeed is thicker than water.

Whatever delicacies a dog is given, it can never reject its natural food, excrement. I 'm glad, my dear, I 'm glad that it is impossible for circumstances to sever you from your natural roots. Your blood is your blood! My blood is in you. Nothing can come between blood bond.

(In front of Lanre, puts forward his hand for a hand-shake; Lanre does so cautiously. He Sits down as he hugs OBONG again)

-Rhahaab, how are you?

RHAHAAB (surprised and suspiciously):
-I am fine and happily settled. And you?

VISITOR (genially):
-I 'm sound in wind and limb.

RHAHAAB (affably):
-It's been quite an age, Ebong.

VISITOR (congenially):
-Yes! Business, my dear is energy sapping and time consuming. It takes up all my time.

RHAHAAB (Lanre clears his throat to speak, but is interrupted, amiably):
-And you still find time to see us? Welcome.

VISITOR (looking as grave as a judge, phlegmatically):
-Well, time is precious. Time is scarce. Tic, tic, tic, it goes; forward ever, backward never, Tic, Tic, Tic. It goes and it waits for no one. However, he who has an important thing to do will surely create time for that.

RHAHAAB (Lanre sits forward, uncomfortably and eagerly, as if what he dreaded the most has finally coast home to roost, creepily):
-What important thing are you hinting at?

VISITOR (rhetorically):

-A crocodile is never disembowelled in the open lest its gorge makes the gorge of onlookers rise. Inside, hedged by eyes inured to such horrors, the skulls and bones of its prey, sometimes, the remains of beloved ones, are sorted out of the carnivore's bowel, before the washed and cleaned gut is offered outside as edible parts.

So, right inside here I called to the hearing of only our ears, as in auricular confession, that we may sort out this issue, without publicity or embarrassment and to the satisfaction of all concerned.

RHAHAAB (ruffled):
-Come back to earth. What important issue?

VISITOR:
-From its fruit a tree is recognized. Once you've seen this child, you've known my father.

RHAHAAB (LANRE'S face is as long as a fiddle, more discomfited):
-Which child?

VISITOR:
-This child and my father are as like as two peas.

RHAHAAB (LANRE, who has seen the straw in the wind looks on, in stunned silence. More disconcerted):
-Don't beat about the bush. Hit the nail on the head: what are you insinuating?

VISITOR (drops the bombshell):
-This child on my laps, in my hands, hugged to my bosom, is mine. My own very child, my blood, my flesh, my biological child. Can't you see the filial affection?

RAHAAB (adversarially):
-Why have you come to make the fur fly in my home?

VISITOR:
-I did not come to raise any dusts here.

RAHAAB: (Lanre enters the room, bleakly):
-Then, don't run your head against a wall. You will only be ploughing the sand.

VISITOR (enthusiastically):
-If the hen lays her eggs, sits on them till they all are ready, hatches chicken, nurses her chick, dares the hawk to the sky, all for them to survive, what should we as humans do to our chick? Throw them away? Am I the lizard, which lays its eggs and never returns to its hatchery?

RHAHAAB (LANRE cringes and signals OBONG with his finger. OBONG leaves the visitor to LANRE who carries him and coddles him. Heavily):
-If you laid any eggs, return to your hatchery; but none of your eggs is incubating here.

VISITOR (soberly):
-I came to make peace. Not to break a home.

RHAHAAB (tartly):
-You couldn't have come to make peace where there is no war.

VISITOR (amicably):
-I did not come to make the feathers fly. I came for a peaceful settlement, to pay your expenditure on my child.
Even a double fold, so I can claim my own child and give him the nurture of his natural father.

RHAHAAB (repulsively):
-Remember! The frog never jumps backwards. Only the dog returns to its vomit. Perish this hair-raising thought of yours.

(*LANRE carries OBONG into his bedroom*)

Your child is not here. Go elsewhere in search for your child.

VISITOR:
-You cannot compare this circumstance with vomit. Nothing is greater than the attraction between father and son. I can do nothing and leave the matter to the dictates of tradition. Our people say: 'Whenever a child grows up, they will trace and return to their origin'.

RHAHAAB (remembers her mother's dream in her spine-chilling moment):
-My child is in his father's house, the father who brought him up.

VISITOR:
-Do not call anyone 'father,' for you have one Father who is in heaven - the origin, the source - represented by the Earthly link, the Earthly father who brought him forth.
Fathership is not determined by caring for a child but only by being the source of the DNA (coded instructions) from which the offspring sprang and developed into whatever he has been programmed to be.
Father means originator, not just the nuturer. Call no one Father except the one linked to the originator and source who also carries spiritual blessings coded in the DNA sequence. His presence in the child's life only

ensures the child's full potential realisation in life for our stars and what we are turned into are coded in our dna sequence.

RHAHAAB:
-DNA apostle, Is it daybreak for DNA advocacy for you now? Some women palm extramaritally begotten children off on their husbands; by stroke of luck or guile or guts the extramarital children are acknowledged as legitimate by their bride price Fathers who are not linked to their source nor carry DNA coded spiritual blessings (enhancing forces) neither did they bring forth the child as you theorise. But they do well in life.

VISITOR:
-As the spirit-kind orders the footsteps of humans through spiritual DNA so do original fathers transmit physical DNA to their children which directs them aright.

So, for a child to achieve full potential, his DNA donor needs to be in his Life to activate the DNA but with an interloper, the DNA will remain dormant with the child's destiny stunted whilst the DNA father, the earthly link will interface with the spiritual origin to catalyse and promote the offspring's full potential actualization to show that among the fathers (bride price, Foster, legal, deadbeat, DNA or real father and acknowledged father), there is the provable father with overriding influence on the child instantiating the fact that among the gods is a real God with overriding power on humans.

RHAHAAB:
-Teacher, it is now daybreak for hackneyed theorems, but spare me these sermons. My child is in his father's house, the father who nurtured him.

VISITOR:

-As the spirit-kind, the source of humankind is entitled to seek for and control human beings so is a DNA father, the representative of the spiritual source, entitled to seek for and take charge of his lost progeny. The DNA father is the one who brought forth the child. He should also nurture or bring up his child.

RHAHAAB:

-You cannot reap where you did not sow. Plough, plant, water, weed, wait before harvest...

VISITOR:

-If I ploughed, planted the seed and gracious nature watereth it, the harvest is still mine.

RHAHAAB:

-You reap what you've sown and watereth and nursed. Can a farmer that watereth not expect harvest? Can a father shirk his responsibilities and still expect harvest? Can an investor fail to invest and expect dividends? Go elsewhere, your harvest is not here. My child is with his father.

VISITOR:

-My blood son, my genetic son, my DNA son needs me as the body needs food.

As the soul is nursed by relationships, the heart is sharpened by companionship, the mind is healed by communion, the body, spirit and soul are uplifted by mutual connectivity and interconnectivity is the soul of our collective will progressing to his will in our lives so is a child's fellowship with his natural father the balm for his spirit because the biological father, his link to the cosmos is the door through Which the child comes into existence, and the root that supports, then waters and ensures the tree bears fruits.

Above all: the prayers of the authentic father for his progenies do not need fasting to bind demons, his blessings do not need piety nor charity to block leakages of proceeds of the offspring's sweat nor sacrifices to loosen the bonded child.

His pronouncements on, binding and loosing of the children are sacrosanct.

His wishes, like the Eagle have wings that carry the offspring over impediments, far above principalities to surmount obstacles; for these reasons, a carer, bride price father, or Foster father can only be ' a substitute father ', at best, a caretaker and cannot replace a deadbeat father, much less a biological Father. These are trite spiritual laws that cannot be interfered with irrespective of the star that is embedded in the DNA sequence.

The DNA father is the intermediary of the ultimate source and is a privileged delegate in the race to relay the DNA sequencing baton showcasing the power of procreation, propagation, and perpetuity in signs and wonders that witness to the ultimate power.

RHAHAAB:

-My son is already loosed, blessed, fruitful; his spirit is already served and satisfied, his demons are already bound by his father even if you say he is a mere caretaker; go elsewhere and offer your sacrament.

VISITOR:

-He could be more; he can do much more under the divine grace induced by fellowship with his sire.

RHAHAAB:
-You did not sire well. Try your luck elsewhere, your free lunch is not here. My child is with his father - call him caretaker if that makes you happy.

VISITOR (dissenting):
-He is not. Remember! Whatever a lion sets its claws on, belongs to the lion, its ineluctable prey. My child is my child and will return to me.

RHAHAAB (dreadfully):
-Don't flog a dead horse. Don't try to move a mountain. Pigs will never fly.

VISITOR (gets up, defiantly):
-I will! Heaven and earth will I move to get my son, I will! Pigs will fly before Thomas' eyes. I will claim my child (walks towards the door, insistently) by hook or by crook: fair'st or foul'st.
From might and main to the black power or the power of money. Even to the end of my tether I will get my child.

(*RHAHAAB reluctantly sees the visitor to the door. At the doorpost, half to herself*)

RHAHAAB (aside):
-Whatever the gods have cast must set. Who can uncast the ominous curse of the gods? We can only accept the verdict of the gods.

(*As the visitor exits, LANRE enters again*)

LANRE (winces, aghast at the development):
-The gods surely use all the elements of life to rule in the affairs of humans. Who is he?

RHAHAAB (defensively):
-A quondam friend.

(*Enter Alice and Beki, the atmosphere is still tense. She changes topic quickly*)

ALICE (with a certain level of sobriety):
-Good evening 'aunty'. How are you and the family?

RHAHAAB (with great solemnity):
-All fine! And you? You are both carrying big books. Where are you coming from?

ALICE (surreptitiously):
-We both went to fellowship.

RHAHAAB (taken aback, with intense earnestness):
-Fellowship? So, you have joined them?

ALICE (with utmost eloquence and gravity):
-Yes. We are now 'born again'.

RHAHAAB:
-What about Rose?

BEKI:
-She is now 'born again' too.

RHAHAAB (with a mirthless smile):
-Rose has also joined them? Where is she now?

BEKI:
-She stayed behind for special prayers with a 'brother'.

RHAHAAB (flabbergasted):
-Which 'brother' is that?

BEKI (Excitedly, volunteers more details):
-That N.C.E. teacher she bought a car for.

RHAHAAB (dumbfounded, mirthlessly):
- She gave a car to a man?

BEKI:
-Yes! To a 'brother'.

RHAHAAB (aside):
-That bait is big enough to catch any fish.
(Then to others) How generous is my dear Rose? How lucky is that brother? Alice, what about the young man who was living with you?

ALICE (soberly):
-Don't mind that idiot. The ingrate left.

RHAHAAB:
-Left you, after feeding and providing roof over his head for years?

ALICE:
-Yes, he left, the ungrateful parasite left.

RHAHAAB (winces at the disgust in her story, then grimly):
-What about the money you loaned him?

ALICE (a little ashamed):
-That one has been settled in court. The judge said since he had no job, he should pay the money at the rate of twenty thousand Naira per month.

RHAHAAB:
-That's ridiculous. Won't you both sit down? Are you so much in hurry?

ALICE (Beki walks to the door):
-Yes! We only dropped in to say hello.

RHAHAAB (ALICE follows BEKI; and then RHA-HAAB follows them, with kod, kod, flip, flop, clicking and clacking noises of their heels on the polished tiles):
-Alright.

ALICE AND BEKI (all wave):
-Bye!

(*Exhuent*)

LANRE (RHAHAAB returns to him):
-Darling, why is it that all these unmarried women usually become 'born again'?

RHAHAAB (holding LANRE'S hand, dallying with the idea of born "againsm"):
-When one realises that she led a sinful life; she confesses her sins, repents and becomes born a new.

LANRE:
-Or, because as nature abhors a vacuum, so must women be dependent on somebody. Those who do not catch a man to depend on, turn to Jesus.

RHAHAAB:
-Not just turning to God, they forsake their old ways, obtain Mercy, have the old stoney heart removed, receive a new heart and become 'born again', a brand-new creature.

LANRE (RHAHAAB sits down on the settee beside him. Simply):

-Just like that? Born again? The physiology, desires and neuro-hormonal impulses in that old body become temperate, born anew? At sunset? At the death knell for all hope? Humans are born to depend on something. Men must depend on their maker or perish, illustrated by the fact that women must depend on men or be violated. That is the grand design of creation. The natural tendency is dependency.

RHAHAAB:

-But dependency predicated on a new WAY, new spirit, simpliciter. It is better late than never. All for protection. Dependency is the padlock, but the key is submissiveness. To be "born again" is to totally submit so that you can inherit full protection. It is necessary for them to be born again. The only way out is for them to be born again.

LANRE:

-When the minefield has been excavated? When the stores are depleted? When the Oasis has been taken over by the desert? When all hope has been drained?

RHAHAAB:

-As long as there is life, there is hope. With God, nothing is impossible: the desert becomes wetland, mountains move, droughts become moisture and famine turns to surplus. Nothing God cannot do. The Lord is good all the Time.

Curtain falls.

ACT THREE. SCENE EIGHT

The spiritual kingdoms control the physical kingdom just as the father's DNA inherited by the child influences the child's development

A SCENE IN THE CHURCH
An uncompleted building provides shelter for these parishioners. The environment is chiefly for those who are desperate or in distress and have no hope or any other place for succour and solace.
About thirty females and fifteen males are in fellowship in the church. Most of the brethrens are in the spirit: some speaking in tongues, some sweating profusely from excessive gyration and vibration, while a few are, somewhat, nonplussed. We meet the service mid-stream.

PASTOR (sweating profusely, fervently):
-The spiritual kingdoms control the physical. The most High rulleth over the Earth. The Highest reigns in the affairs of His people. The watchers watch over the lost. The power of the kingdom of darkness is over the disobedient. The power of binding and loosing belongs to the kingdom of Light. The naunces of spiritual powers, too deep for our understanding, is as varied as darkness and light, and as wide as the gulf between life and death Let us pray!

(Everyone closes their eyes)

Oh! Lord! Keep watch and ward thy flock against the decoy of the devil. Few as we are, we're gathered in thy name. Lord! As we feel thy presence here among us now, may you direct us on what to do, in thy holy name.

(Everybody answers in a chorus):
-Amen!

PASTOR:
-We shall all sing hymn number 393.

(All hymnals are opened. All sing in a chorus as the pastor directs with a wave of his hand after humming the first verse of the song once)

How wonderful! Oh! What wondrous news! For a sinner to abandon sin, shun Satan, to 'escape from everlasting fire, and turn to God for eternal life in heaven.

PASTOR (still in the spirit, impassioned):
-We shall all pray together.

(All eyes are closed. Everybody starts to pray variously and loudly at the same time. Suddenly, ROSE starts shaking her body all over like a green fly. She cries as if she's in pain and still shaking)

ROSE (shakes all over like a person in epileptic fit, but she's still in the standing position)
-Blaa blaa blaa blaa, tii tii tii tii, Blaa blaa blaa blaa, tii tii tii tii. Blaa blaa blaa blaa, tii tii tii tii, Blaa blaa blaa blaa, tii tii tii tii.

PASTOR (calmly. ROSE is not interrupted, she continues shaking her body, stamps her foot on the floor and cries, apparently oblivious of her surroundings):
-The spirit of the lord is upon our sister.
(Pointing to Rose) She is talking in tongues as she is seeing vision now. Is there anybody in this flock who has the hands of the Lord upon him, to interpret to us God's command as revealed to us through our sister?

ALICE (eagerly, lifts up her hand. ROSE continues her writhing movement without intermission):
-Yes!

PASTOR (approvingly. ROSE's cries are in the background, rising to its crescendo. Gestures to ALICE):
-Yes, sister, interpret to us the Lord's bidding.

ROSE (still in her fit of writhing motions):
-Blaa blaa blaa blaa, tii tii tii tii. Blaa blaa blaa blaa, tii tii tii tii.

ALICE (play-acting with uncommon seriousness, ROSE's noise is still in the background. Now at its apogee, rhythmically, to rhyme with ROSE's prayer, mimes her prayer):
- 'Brother' Titus, 'Brother' Titus! 'Brother' Titus, 'Brother' Titus.

ROSE (her 'shaking' is getting worse):
-Blaa blaa blaa blaa, tii tii tii tii, Blaa blaa blaa blaa, tii tii tii tii.

ALICE (most eyes are closed. But the eyes of the doubting Thomases are still prying; every other person in the congregation is silent except ROSE):
- 'Brother' Titus, 'brother' Titus, 'Brother' Titus, 'brother' Titus.

ROSE (her fit is still in its apogee, even writhing in pains now):
-Lorda Raiwai wai, Lorda Raiwai wai, Lorda Raiwai wai, Lorda Raiwai wai.

ALICE (in intense animation, with Rose's voice still in the background, interprets):

-The Lord has chosen Rose for you as a wife, the Lord has chosen Rose for you as a wife.

'Brother' Titus, 'brother' Titus, the Lord has chosen Rose for you as a wife, the Lord has chosen Rose for you as a wife.

'Brother' Titus, 'brother' Titus, the Lord has appointed Rose as your wife!

(*This continues for some time, until Rose eventually calms down. She is sweating and gasping for breath, as if she has just stopped convulsing. She is prostrate on the floor right now. Two or three ushers are beside her, ensuring that no harm occasioned her from the fall*)

PASTOR (sedately):
- (All is calm now; everyone is petrified) We have just received a message from the lord for our brother, Titus. Who is brother Titus?

(*Initially disinclined, then a hand is up from among people in the congregation*)

Brother Titus, our sister here (points to Rose) has been chosen as your wife by the Lord. Praise be to him!

(All except Titus chorus):
-Amen!

TITUS (first, with a comic gesture of disbelief, then, overwhelmed with amazement, argumentatively):
-Pastor, this very morning, a sister told me that she dreamt, and God showed me to her as her husband.
This afternoon, another sister said a Pastor had prophesied that a marriage relationship will be established between us. And now, the evening of the same day, yet

262

another sister has been appointed to me as a wife, as revealed to her in a vision.

Is our God the author of confusion or does he want me to be a polygamist?

(*Everyone looks stunned and confounded, with some murmuring*)

PASTOR (in a befuddled state and not knowing what to say, then suddenly):

-No! The Lord is not an author of confusion. And he does not want you to be a polygamist. Return right now to your room and pray earnestly to the Lord, ask him to guide and direct you, to show you who He has truly appointed to be your wife.

Earnestly seek the face of the Lord, search his words, from the old to the New Testament, ask His Son, what happens here today, is it in conformity with his teaching?

(*After a moment of bewilderment, dawdled some minutes away, Titus exits*)

PASTOR:

-We shall now sing, closing hymn number 399.

(Everyone opens hymnals. The pastor hums. Everyone sings): What shall I use to build a house for God?

(Choir master) Use cement to build a house for God.

(Everyone) No! No! Cement can't build a house for God.

(Pastor) What shall I use to build a house for God?

(Choir master) Use stones to build a house for God.

(Everyone) No! No! Stones can't lay a good foundation for a house for God.

(Pastor) What shall I use to build a house for God?

(Choir master) Use iron to build a house for God.

(Everyone) No! No! Iron can't lay a strong enough foundation for a house for God.

(Pastor) What shall I use to build a house for God?

(Choir master) Use Gold to build a house for God.

(Everyone) No! No! Gold can't build a house for God.

(Pastor) What shall I use to build a house for God?

(Choir master) Use Love to build a house for God.

(Everyone) Yes! Yes! Only love can build a house for God.

(Everyone else is completely carried away by the song. Then, stealthily, ROSE exits)

PASTOR:

-A brother should lead us in a short closing prayer.

A BROTHER:

-Let us pray. Lord! May thy will be done. We gathered here in thy name. Now, we are imbued with thy Holy Spirit. Stand by us, oh Lord, so that we can keep thy commandments against the wishes of Satan. Amen (Everyone, in a chorus)

(All the congregants disperse. The curtain mechanically falls and rises. We see BROTHER TITUS, in his one room apartment, praying frantically. The environment smells of poverty. We can see poverty boldly written on his face)

BROTHER TITUS (still with a befuddled demeanour, effusively):

-My Lord, Oh! Ye merciful father. Maker of heaven and earth. You made man and woman and bid them: 'multiply and be fruitful'.

You bid us to choose from among ourselves husband and wife, and to live as such in happy and blessed families.

(ROSE arrives, meets BROTHER TITUS'S door ajar and sees him praying with wild excitement. She steals into his room without disturbing him, and sits on the bed)

BROTHER TITUS (still praying, as if he is possessed):

-My Lord! My God! I had problems in the past, I had difficult decisions to make before. In your infinite wisdom, you always showed and directed me on the best thing to do. Loving father.

(Stamps his foot on the floor. ROSE is still in the room, without distracting him)

Now! Again! I need your help on the choice of a life partner. The choice of a wife on earth is the most important thing to a man in this life.

If he makes the right choice, he lives in peace, and happily all the days of his life. If he takes a wrong step, he uses his hands to buy and put burning charcoal in his pocket, and then he roasts in fire all his life. Lord! God!

(Asks earnestly)

Direct me to choose a woman that will give me peace all my life, not the one that will be like burning charcoal in my pocket, nor the one that will be poison to my heart, neither the one that will make me derail and backslide from following you.

You have never failed me before! You promised and led your people, Israel to their rest. Choose for me a good woman as a wife, my own rest. The best from among your flock, so that together we shall do great exploits in your vineyard! Amen!

(*He opens his eyes and suddenly sees ROSE, quite unexpectedly, surprised*)

The Lord is wonderful! So, you are here!

ROSE (smiles at him, bewitchingly):
-The Lord directed me to come here right now.

BROTHER TITUS (mesmerised):
-Praise the Lord! So, are you the one He has chosen for me? Chosen for me, chosen as my wife? May his name be praised!

ROSE (quaintly):
-Yes! He's the same God who directed me to give you a car, who now gives me to you as a wife - the way He gave Eve to Adam. He is a generous God! He is a giver per excellence.

BROTHER TITUS (dazed and still receives the miracle with a grain of salt):
-Providing a wife is one, the dowry and accommodation are still pending, but may his name be praised all the same! Amen!

(Both answer in unison):
-Amen!

ROSE (with cool unction. Faithfully):
-He who makes the way provides the means. He has provided you a wife. Is dowry or accommodation impossible for him to provide? Screw your faith to the sticking

place for he is too faithful not to meet you at the point of your needs.

BROTHER TITUS (still enchanted):
-With him nothing is impossible.

ROSE:
-The earth and the fullness thereof belong to him. I 've bought everything we will need for our wedding. I have bought everything we will need in our family. You will not spend any money at all. As the head of the family, I leave you to fix the date for the wedding.

BROTHER TITUS (still sober and taken aback, sceptically):
-How come you have already completed the preparation for the wedding when...?

ROSE (interrupts, while he is still spellbound):
-I only do as the Lord directs. He showed you to me... as a husband since. He asked me to wait... until when He would enter into your heart and convince you miraculously as he did today, just the way he did to Paul.

BROTHER TITUS (soberly):
-Well! Everything has been so miraculous. I am confounded, in fact...

ROSE (cuts in, mesmerizingly):
-God works miraculously. His ways transgress our ken. And his deeds should not be questioned. What he has willed has been willed and cannot be changed.

BROTHER TITUS (in a besotted manner):
-Everything! I just can't explain. The way you gave me a car: I couldn't believe it. If I saw manna falling from

267

heaven, it would be more believable than hearing that in this austere time, someone is giving out her car.

Then the spirit came on you. Satan almost made me question the works of God. Then I asked him to show me a wife and miraculously, you appeared to me.

All these things are inscrutable.

ROSE (adding more pressure, quaintly):
-Everything is the work of God. What he has willed, so may it be! Try as he may, Satan will never succeed.

BROTHER TITUS (as if recovering from a spell):
-As for our wedding date, we will fix that later.

ROSE (too overwrought to comport herself, hems, coughs, gladly):
-You are my King. I am at your command. It's alright by me any date you choose. I'll return home. It's been long since I've been out.

BROTHER TITUS (seeing ROSE off to the door, as she catwalks, loftily):
-May the good Lord direct and protect us. Amen! (Chorus both) Till we see in fellowship tomorrow. Bye, my love.

(ROSE waves back):
-Bye!

ROSE (excitedly, as she walks away, half in supplication, thoughtfully):
-Can this be true, this dream? This yearn, this endless yearning of mine, materializing? Or, am I dreaming? Where am I now? (yawns)

(Looks round, jumps up, shouts and pinches herself as if to confirm she is not dreaming)

No! no! no! I am not dreaming, this is reality. As real as a smile. I have won for myself a man that I can use at least as a swagger stick (demonstrates the way a soldier walks majestically with a walking stick).

I 've tasted the slavery of marriage and savoured freedom from dependency, and now know that freedom indeed, is made perfect or is concreted in dependency.

As the cow needs its tail, a woman needs a man. As water quenches thirst, so are the desires of a woman quenched by man. As aroma whets the appetite, so does man whet a woman's feelings. As wine is the aperitif to the palate so is man the digestif to the soul of women.

As babies need their mothers, a woman needs a husband. As Israel survives attacks because she depends on America, so is a woman spared defilement by violators because she has a husband, practical corroborations to convince us that there is strength in dependency, there's protection in dependency.

Marriage is the university universal sans borders that proves that, for by wife's dependence on husband she is saved from attacks, harassment, humiliation, and defilement; in the same way, humans are saved from being consumed by transcendent beings, so long as they depend solely on the supreme being.

For the triune of husband, wife and violators typifies or instantiates the trio of Supreme being, Human being and Supramundane being in versity to prove the law of Trinity:

Unless the weak (UKRAINE) gets the protection of the strongest (NATO), they will be devoured by the strong (RUSSIA). Today, I have won my own man, my defender, my protector. I have conquered vulnerability; I have conquered my shame. I have conquered the world. I have come to this ultimate understanding: unless humans depend on God, they stand consumed as epitomised by the fact that unless women depend on their husbands, they stand violated.

I have won freedom on the altar of dependency, for humans shall be free only in dependency, according to the agreement in purpose by the gods. What the gods have set down, no human can change.

(Happily):
-Now I am a complete woman.
(Jumps up and shouts crazily) I have won a man.

(*Congratulates herself by thumping her chest*)

The lizard says: 'If it falls from the very height of the Iroko tree and hits the hard ground baaang! Then looks round and sees nobody who is impressed enough to say well done, it will praise itself because that is not a mean feat for an ordinary lizard'.

(*ROSE, in high glee, cut capers*)

Like the lizard, I say: 'Beautiful woman, you have done well! Now, I feel as if my world is complete. I now have a man of my own. I am a complete woman. I now have my own husband.

(*Thinks again*)

Any time I want, I have one at home. Any man that harasses me outside, I will tell him that I have one at home, his very type.

Any woman that teases me, I will let her know that I have one at home, young, vibrant, long. I have one at home, in hot or cold season. I have one at home: for security, psychological or financial support. I have one at home. It will redound to my present status.

So, instead of a pet-dog, to scare away intruders, I now have a pet-man to ward off invaders. This is not a mean feat. I am now a secured territory, a reserved area, exclusive, free from general use.

Truly, He has not called the house of Jacob to serve him in vain. It pays to be born again: you become smarter, a new creature.

(*As if she remembers something*)

His marrying me is on the knees of the gods. Except they build, the builder builds in vain, except they watch over the city, the watchmen watch in vain. Who says a thing and it comes to pass except it is the CONSENSUS of the gods?

The Fate of humans is dependent on vetting by the gods. Getting a husband nowadays is a lottery.

It is not as sure as the Mercies of David. Nor as sure as Sunrise following sunset? Neither as sure as dawn following dusk. I must not count my chicken before they are hatched.

There's many a slip 'twixt the cup and the lip. First, I must consolidate my gains. I must not let any grass grow under my feet. My find must first concrete because fast bind is fast found, especially for someone who has publicly crucified dependence and put the institution of marriage to shame.

Black out as curtain falls.

ACT THREE. SCENE NINE

Fatherhood is not simply being the carer or care-taker but the originator, the source of DNA (in-structions, the invisible power) that directs a child's development, akin to the spirit-kind that controls humankind

A SCENE IN THE APPEAL COURT
Morning session. The court is packed full of people. A large number of them are standing inside and outside the court room. Journalists and camera men are very busy clicking their equipment. We meet the session mid-stream, with LANRE in the witness-box

DEFENCE LAWYER:
-Are you married to the mother of this young star whose paternity is being disputed in this court now?

(*Points to master OBONG seated beside his mother in the court room*)

LANRE:
-Yes, married for seven years.

DEFENCE LAWYER:
-Legally married?

LANRE:
-Traditionally, religiously and legally married to the mother of my first child, Obong.

DEFENCE LAWYER:
-With marriage certificates?

LANRE:

-Yes! With all the documents.

DEFENCE LAWYER:

-Where are the marriage documents?

LANRE (hands them over to him, eagerly):

-Here are the certificates.

DEFENCE LAWYER (collects, studies and nods with a smile):

-These may be received in evidence as exhibits A1 and A2.

(*Hands the certificates over to the judge. The judge looks at the certificates studiously, purrs his approval, hands them over to the counsel for the appellant, who only takes a glance at them before passing them over to the court officer*)

DEFENCE LAWYER:

-You said earlier on, in the course of this defence that the child is talented.

LANRE:

-Yes! He's very talented. That's why he won international awards at the tender age of seven.

DEFENCE LAWYER:

-Who discovered his talents?

LANRE:

-I discovered his unusual abilities when he was very young.

DEFENCE LAWYER:
-How did he develop the talents?

LANRE:
-I devoted every minute of my leisure time to nursing his talents, coached him until he was able to perform the feat that sent everybody running after him.

(*Everyone bursts out laughing*)

DEFENCE LAWYER:
-So, you think it's because of the child's success that the appellant in this case wants to have a piece of the cake?

LANRE (another outburst of laughter and murmuring is heard in the court room):
-Yes, of course! Everyone likes to identify with success. The litigant wants to reap where he did not sow. He wants a piece of the pie.

(*The laughter infects everyone in the court room again*)

DEFENCE LAWYER:
-Has his talent been fully developed by now?

LANRE:
-Far from being fully developed. I have a plan of working with him to enable him to develop his potentialities to the fullest.

DEFENCE LAWYER:
-Can any other person help him do that as well as you have been doing?

LANRE:

-Not at all, especially for someone that is strange to him. I understand him from his infancy till date. I have been working with him. I know best about his abilities.

DEFENCE LAWYER (presumably):

-So, will his capabilities greatly suffer if he is detached from you now?

LANRE (presumptively):

-Yes! Expectedly so. Firstly, such an overwhelming psychological trauma will completely demoralize him and may even destroy him.

DEFENCE LAWYER:

-So, would the child be worse off should such an unfortunate destiny destruction occur?

LANRE:

-Even the society would be worse off for it, because the laurels he wins for his country would stop coming.

DEFENCE LAWYER (winningly):

-My learned friend, you may cross-examine my client.

COUNSEL FOR THE APPELLANT (springs up to his feet, eagerly):

-Mr Lanre Aso, you said your blood group is A?

LANRE (certainly):

-Yes sir.

COUNSEL FOR THE APPELLANT:

-When did you have your blood group tested?

LANRE:

-My blood group has been tested at many instances.

COUNSEL FOR THE APPELLANT:

-What are those instances?

LANRE:

-Once, I just wanted to know my blood group.

COUNSEL FOR THE APPELLANT:

-And the other instances?

LANRE:

-I can't quite recollect why I had to check my blood group.

COUNSEL FOR THE APPELLANT:

-Was it when you disputed being the father of master Obong seven years ago in a court?

LANRE (reflectively):

-I did not dispute being Obong's father. I just wanted to be very sure I was really his father before marrying his mother.

COUNSEL FOR THE APPELLANT:

-So, you did then entertain the fear that the child you were about to assume fatherhood of might after all be someone's else's?

LANRE:

-No, I only wanted to be perfectly sure that the child was mine.

COUNSEL FOR THE APPELLANT:
-I see. Listen to this. (Presses a button on a tape-recorder)

SOUND FROM THE TAPE RECORDER:
-Because I am convinced that the child is not mine.

COUNSEL FOR THE APPELLANT:
-That is your voice, isn't it?

LANRE (like a thunderbolt):
-Yes, it is my voice.

COUNSEL FOR THE APPELLANT:
-Which child were you referring to, master Obong?

LANRE (like a bombshell):
-Yes, but…

(*Counsel for the appellant presses a button on the tape-recorder again*)

SOUND FROM THE TAPE RECORDER:
-The results confirmed that the child whose blood was tested inherited the blood gene 'A' from his father.

COUNSEL FOR THE APPELLANT:
-Whose voice is that?

LANRE:
-That is the voice of the laboratory expert who confirmed that I inherited blood gene 'A', which I passed on to my son, Obong, which explains why we both have the same blood group.

COUNSEL FOR THE APPELLANT:
-Did that genetic expert not also tell you in that court that master Obong could have inherited that gene 'A' from any other man who had same gene in his blood?

LANRE:
-I don't know how that could possibly be.

COUNSEL FOR THE APPELLANT:
-In exactly the same way you think you transferred that gene to the boy. And you said you're married to Obong's mother?

LANRE (almost mockingly):
-Yes.

COUNSEL FOR THE APPELLANT:
-When did you marry her? Was it before or after Obong's birth?

LANRE:
-After his birth.

COUNSEL FOR THE APPELLANT:
-How long after?

LANRE:
-One year.

COUNSEL FOR THE APPELLANT:
-So, the child was born out of wed-lock?

DEFENCE LAWYER (jumps to his feet, formidably):
-Objection my lord! That question is irrelevant. The case before this court is not to determine whether master

Obong is an illegitimate child or not, but to determine whether the litigant is his natural father or not.

JUDGE (gravely):
-Objection sustained.

COUNSEL FOR THE APPELLANT:
-So, it took you that long to try and ascertain that the child was yours or not?

LANRE:
-No. I got married only when I was financially ready to do so.

COUNSEL FOR THE APPELLANT (in high spirits):
-My lord! I have no more questions for him.
JUDGE:

-You may return to your seat.

(*Lanre leaves the witness-box, sweating*)

COUNSEL FOR THE APPELLANT (springs to his feet):
-I now call mister Ebong to the witness-box.

(*EBONG mounts the witness box*)

COURT OFFICER:
-Are you a Christian or a Muslim?

EBONG:
-I'm a Christian.

COURT OFFICER:
-Take this Bible in your right hand and read this.

EBONG (takes the Bible in his right hand, lifts up his right hand and reads the inscriptions on the card):

-The evidence I shall give shall be the truth, the whole truth, and nothing but the truth.

COUNSEL FOR THE APPELLANT:

-Mister Ebong, you know the mother of the child whose paternity is being disputed now?

EBONG:

-I know her very, very well.

COUNSEL FOR THE APPELLANT:

-How do you know her?

EBONG:

-She has been my girlfriend for many years.

COUNSEL FOR THE APPELLANT:

-Supposing Mrs. R. Aso denies ever being your girl-friend or ever knowing you?

EBONG:

-She cannot, in good conscience, deny that she has been my girlfriend for many years. And I doubt whether in all sincerity, she can deny that master Obong is my child. I have photographs that will prove that we were intimately in love with each other for many years.

COUNSEL FOR THE APPELLANT:

-Pictures? What type of pictures?

EBONG:

-Pictures of moments she and I had together that will convince anybody that we both know each other very, very well.

(*Brings out photographs from his pocket and hands them over to his Lawyer. Rhahaab frowns*)

COUNSEL FOR THE APPELLANT (looks at the photographs, admiringly):
-Pictures of master Obong's mother, when she was a young girl, beautifully dressed and seated on your lap in your room. This is your room in the background. Is my guess right?

EBONG:
-Yes! You are quite right. The first one was my room in my father's house and the second one was in my room when I packed into my first personal house.

COUNSEL FOR THE APPELLANT (nods, convincingly):
-The photographs, like silence, speak volumes for themselves and are convincing enough. They may be admitted in evidence as exhibits B2 and B3.

(*Hands the photographs over to the Judge, who studies them in detail before handing them over to the defence lawyer who, in turn, passes them over to the Court Officer*)

For how many years have you been in friendship with Obong's mother?

EBONG:
-For five long years. We even promised to marry each other.

COUNSEL FOR THE APPELLANT:
-And why didn't you eventually marry her?

EBONG:

-Every man has an Eve, made from his ribs, meant to be his better-half, what some people call Miss Right. While searching and waiting for our right person, we all make do with the nearest person to our ideal partners.

COUNSEL FOR THE APPELLANT:

-So, you left her and married another person who best fitted into your idea of a wife when you met one?

EBONG:

-Exactly! I married My Miss Right, when I eventually found her.

COUNSEL FOR THE APPELLANT:

-And discarded your Miss Wrong, but by then, did you know she was carrying your baby?

EBONG:

-No! Not at all. She did not tell me, probably because she knew I was already bent on marrying another person.

COUNSEL FOR THE APPELLANT:

-My learned friend, you may cross-examine my client.

COUNSEL FOR THE RESPONDENT:

-Mr. Ebong, are you married?

EBONG:
-Yes.

COUNSEL FOR THE RESPONDENT:
-Do you have children?

EBONG:
-No.

COUNSEL FOR THE RESPONDENT:
-Is that the Karma of your ill-treatment of your former girlfriend?

EBONG:
-I don't know anything about Karma.

COUNSEL FOR THE RESPONDENT:
-Is that why you now want to assume fatherhood of another person's child?

COUNSEL FOR THE APPELLANT:
-Objection my Lord, my client is ridiculed by this line of questioning.

JUDGE (gravely):
-Objection sustained.

DEFENCE LAWYER (springs up, surprisingly):
-I have no more questions for him.

JUDGE (nods):
-Young man, you may return to your seat.

(*EBONG returns to his seat*)

COUNSEL FOR THE APPELLANT:
-I now call on Professor Dakkada.

(*PROFESSOR DAKKADA mounts the witness –box*)

COURT OFFICER:
-What is your religion?

PROF:
-What do you mean by "my religion"?

COURT OFFICER (surprised, amidst murmuring in the Court room):
-What is your faith, who do you worship? Are you a Christian or a Muslim?

PROF (as serious as a dead man):
-None of the above.

COURT OFFICER:
-Will you then like to affirm?

PROF:
-Yes.

COURT OFFICER:
-Lift your right hand and read this affirmation.

PROF (lifts up his hand and reads):
-I affirm that the evidence I shall give shall be the truth, the whole truth, and nothing but the truth.

COUNSEL FOR THE APPELLANT:
-You are the head of Research Institute for Human Genetics?

PROF:
-You are right.

COUNSEL FOR THE APPELLANT:
-You are a fellow of the International Society of Genetic Scientists?

PROF:
-You are right as well.

COUNSEL FOR THE APPELLANT:
-What are your qualifications?

PROF:

-M. B.; B. S.; MSC.; PHD (Genetics); F.I.S.G.; DSC.

COUNSEL FOR THE APPELLANT:

-So, you are also a medical doctor?

PROF:

-Yes. I'm a medical practitioner, but I specialized in Human Genetics.

COUNSEL FOR THE APPELLANT:

-Are you aware of the details of this case?

PROF:

-Yes, I'm well aware of the details of this case.

COUNSEL FOR THE APPELLANT:

-You carried out blood tests on the defendant, the appellant and the child whose paternity is being disputed now?

PROF:

-Yes.

COUNSEL FOR THE APPELLANT:

-What is the child's blood group?

PROF:

-Master Obong's blood has 'A' and 'B' genes. The mother's group is 'B'

COUNSEL FOR THE APPELLANT:

-Can you explain the medical term 'genotype' to us non-medical professionals?

PROF:

-A genotype is a combination of inherited substances called genes.

COUNSEL FOR THE APPELLANT:

-What is the defendant's blood group?

PROF:

-The defendant's group is 'A'.

COUNSEL FOR THE APPELLANT:

-So, the respondent and the appellant have the same genotype?

PROF:

-Yes! The respondent and appellant have the same group, 'A'.

COUNSEL FOR THE APPELLANT:

-What does this your laboratory finding mean?

PROF:

-The laboratory tests I carried out confirmed that master Obong inherited the gene 'B' from his mother and gene 'A' from his father, because any gene present in a child but not present in the mother must be present in the father.

COUNSEL FOR THE APPELLANT:

-So, master Obong could have inherited the gene 'A' either from the appellant or from the respondent?

PROF:

-Master Obong inherited the gene 'A' only from his father.

COUNSEL FOR THE APPELLANT:
-Who did Obong inherit the gene 'A' from?

PROF:
-He inherited the gene from his father.

COUNSEL FOR THE APPELLANT (confused, not knowing what else to ask):
-So, in your opinion, Prof., based on your scientific test and knowledge, who is the father of master Ogbon?

DEFENCE LAWYER (springs to his feet with alacrity, impetuously):
-Objection, my Lord! That is presumptive. The answer constitutes a usurpation of the duty of this court. It is the duty of this court to determine who the child's father is.

JUDGE (gravely):
-Objection sustained.

COUNSEL FOR THE APPELLANT:
- Professor Dakkada, what is the meaning of Daddy?

PROF. DAKKADA:
- In Ibibio language, Da ddi means: bring, provide for me.

COUNSEL FOR THE APPELLANT:
-So, in English language, what does Daddy mean?

PROF. DAKKADA:
-Daddy means the provider of my daily needs.

COUNSEL FOR THE APPELLANT:
-Is that the meaning of Father?

PROF. DAKKADA:

-Father is not just the provider, but the originator, the source of DNA (instructions, the invisible power), the verifiable factor that influences or directs a child's development parallel with and validating the unseen forces that order the footsteps of human beings.

The DNA Father is not just the carer, but the door through Which the child comes into existence, the confirmation of an ultimate source, the prove of an ultimate POWER, the God that the offspring sees and believes in the God he has never seen, the provider that never fails that makes him believe in the promise keeper, the roots through which the tree receives water to ensures it bears fruits.

The real father is girded with the offspring's blessings coded in his DNA; he is the only one who can transmit this DNA to his offspring and so cannot be traded with a substitute father just like the true God that cannot be replaced by other gods because our destinies are in his hands.

The real father's prayers for his offspring do not need fasting to bind the demons, his blessings do not need piousness to block holes that drain proceeds of the offspring's sweat, nor sacrifices to loosen the bonded.

His pronouncements on, binding and loosing of the children are sacrosanct.

His wishes have wings that carry the offspring over impediments, far above principalities to surmount obstacles.

The spirits know this and so reveal to humanity that the DNA father is the authentic father overriding the ancestors' doctrine of necessity' which sees bride price fathers, Foster fathers, carers, acknowledged fathers as substitute fathers, to show that among the fathers, there is the provable father, duplicating the template in the spirit realm: among the gods is a real God.

COUNSEL FOR THE RESPONDENT:
-Objection my Lord, my learned friend is turning the court into a comedy theatre of the absurd and poetry recitation concert. This is not a court of theoretical postulations but a court of provable facts.

JUDGE (laughter by all):
-As food fills the stomach and satiates the appetite, so is comedy food for the soul, and laughter is the medicine that heals the mind just as praise and worship provide balm for troubled spirit; so, comedy is needed in this temporal Court.
Objection is overruled but direct your questions to establishing the Paternity of the child.

COUNSEL FOR THE APPELLANT:
-Prof. Dakkada, In this instance, how do you determine THE PROVABLE FATHER from all the men who have gene A? Is it possible for Obong to have inherited that gene 'A' from two persons, the appellant and respondent, jointly?

PROF:
-Certain things never happen jointly: salvation, dying...No! Joint fertilisation is unknown in reproduction, species propagation and human perpetuity. Pellucida penetration is pellet specific, except in human's ultimate fantasy. There is this 'Ibuoro' people's saying: two penises can't penetrate one human orifice at the same time. So, outside the fantasy world, two men cannot sire one child.

290

(*Everyone in the Court room mur-
murs...Prof...Prof...Prof...come down to our level. Then
short silence*)

(Looks askance at the lawyer)
It has been confirmed that only one male egg fertilizes
one female egg. So, he inherited that gene 'A' from only
one man: his father.

COUNSEL FOR THE APPELANT (at his wit's end):
-In this circumstance, where there is the possibility of
either of two persons being the donor of the disputed
gene, are there no methods of actually determining who
the real donor of the gene 'A' is?

PROF:
-This is not that rare case that happens in fantasyland.
That was why I subjected the blood specimens to further
analysis.

COUNSEL FOR THE APPELLANT:
-What were the results of the analyses?

PROF:
-I discovered a rare familial gene designated "delta" in
master Obong's blood. This rare inheritable family gene,
delta, was first identified in Mister Ebong's father as was
documented in the celebrated case of Ebong v. s. Philips.
That same gene was also found in Ebong's grandfather
in the course of that same case, Ebong v. s. Philips. This
rare family gene present in both Master Obong and the
appellant's forefathers was also found in the appellant.

COUNSEL FOR THE APPELLANT (relieved):
-So, Master Obong inherited the rare family gene from
the appellant's ancestors?

PROF:

-Yes! Along with other blood factors present in both the child and the appellant but not in the respondent.

COUNSEL FOR THE APPELLANT:

-Where are the laboratory reports for these findings?

(The Prof. hands them over to him. He takes a cursory glance at them, nods his head affirmatively)

This may be admitted in evidence as exhibit C1 and C2.

(Passes the reports over to the Judge, who peruses the documents page after page)

My learned friend, you may cross examine the witness.

DEFENCE LAWYER (down cast):

-I have no questions for him.

(The curtain mechanically rises and falls. We see the Judge delivering his judgement)

JUDGE (gravely):

-As alleged and established in evidence before this court, Mr. Ebong, you are the biological father of this talented lad. But, excising him now from the man who has brought him up to an enviable prospect, will be devastating to his future and psychologically damaging to his development. And humanity will be worse off if we do not act judiciously.

Therefore, in this circumstance, he will continue to live with Mrs Rhahaab Aso until he attains the age when he will be able to decide who he will live with.

(The court rises, the judge retires; people are murmuring as they come out of the Court room. We see RHAHAAB and ROSE, each holding master Ogbon's hand as they emerge from the court room, talking excitedly)

ROSE (in a triumphal manner):

-This same stage shall be reset. This same drama shall be recast all over the earth: in hamlets, villages, cities or towns, in countries, empires or kingdoms, on all the continents of the earth.

This judgement, this precedence shall be delivered everywhere, every day.

Now henceforth, where a child lives and grows is with the mother, till the child is mature to make their choices. That right is not vested in the man, especially the one who runs away from his responsibilities, only to show up when it is harvest time.

And not the man deciding which child he chooses to father and which he does not.

Curtain falls

ACT THREE. SCENE TEN

Humans are the ball in the ping-pong game of the gods. Each is created specced to purpose, plumaged and deplumed, pillified in the pillory, pilloried and pounced on until drilled into usable tool of either of the rival kingdoms of the gods: for this very reason – to shew in thee my power; and to proclaim my name – have I raised up (EX.9^{16}).

...But to sit on my right hand, and on my left, is not mine to give, but it shall be given to them for whom it is prepared of my father (MATH. 20^{23}),

"See, I have made thee a god to Pharaoh... (God said to Moses)..." (EXODUS 7^1).

So did he drill David into a king and a liberator of his people. And Jonah a preacher in Nineveh. And Samson, an object of scorn to his enemies.

We are what we are wired and meant to be; we are sequenced to play the part we are made to play – hence the DNA sequencing. Each sequence a spec, a role to play for a cast. Each person a narrator of an aspect of the diverse powers of the spirit-kind. Each live a paragraph in the narration of the infinite powers of the spirit-kind. All, together, campaigners of the manifest aura of omnipotence of the spirit-kind.

A SCENE IN THE CHURCH

The church is packed full of invitees. The atmosphere is that of uncertainty. The environment is not particularly captivating or inspiring. The earliest comers are getting impatient

295

FIRST INVITEE (to his health officer-in-charge, impatiently):

-You brought me here! If this thing is not taking place any longer, tell me, I have other important things to do. I cannot wait here indefinitely.

HIS HEALTH OFFICER IN-CHARGE (pleadingly):

-A little more patience. Take it easy. Let me find out what is amiss.

ROSE (Rose, who heard this, comes forward to address her invitees, soberly):

-Ladies and Gentlemen! Please, exercise a little more patience. My parents, who encountered a little traffic hold-up, will arrive shortly. Then, everything will be according to schedule.

(*An attendant interrupts ROSE by tapping her on the shoulder. She is summoned to the vestry. Our attention is arrested by two female invitees whispering to themselves. They are among the people in the congregation, and they sit near the dressing room behind the vestry*)

FIRST LADY INVITEE:

- Wedding bell everywhere, not a gown for me. Who did this to me?

SECOND LADY INVITEE:

- From the beginning, it was so, marriage is not for every woman. The wedding gown is not for every damsel as heaven is not for every human being.

FIRST LADY INVITEE (points at a wedding gown in the dressing room. Curiously):

-See, our 'in-charge' even came with a wedding gown. I used to think the wedding gown is meant only for virgins.

SECOND LADY INVITEE (inquisitively):
-Is she not a virgin?

FIRST LADY INVITEE (intrusively):
-Virgin Ke? Somebody who has given birth to three children and done abortions countless number of times?

SECOND LADY INVITEE (didactically):
-If being a virgin were a precondition for wearing the nuptial gown, then no girl is qualified to wear the wedding gown. I can swear that there is no girl of marriage age nowadays who has not done abortion more than once. Abortion is now the first baptism of the girl-child.

FIRST LADY INVITEE (fluidly):
-The wedding gown symbolises innocence, naturalness, and viridity. The veil covers chastity.

The bride price is the reward of purity, the confirmation of the value of the woman, the ratification of the marriage, the stabiliser of the union, the prize of self-control, and the award for obedience and discipline.

Virginity, marriage and faithfulness to only one man to the exclusion of all other men are instantiations of provable faithfulness to only one God to the exclusion of all other gods.

Virginity, the unpunctured, uncontaminated state, sealed by the cistern of blood, puncturable to bond two souls by blood covenant.

Virginity breeds dignity, and is the confirmation of Faithfulness, proof of chastity, documentation of celibacy, attestation of innocence, authentication of purity, affirmation of self-restraint, evidence of fidelity, the seal of obedience, the badge of trust-worthiness, the indicator of loyalty, Verification of steadfastness, the certificate of reliability and the achievement of only determined minds.

And our in-charge is devoid of all and not entitled to that recompense of honour or prize.

Virginity is the passport to high demand in marriage, the protection under a husband just as faith is the passport to heaven, the protection under God.

Women still wear wedding gown nowadays, undeservedly because there is no way our ministers can tell which girl has not done abortions.

SECOND LADY INVITEE (posits):
-Every girl does abortions. Everybody knows that being a virgin is not a precondition for wearing the wedding gown. Where did you buy that wrong idea from? That is why no one insists on medical or practical virginity test before marriage anymore. In this dispensation, the society accepts and permits and encourages sale or loss of virginity, society and dispensation change, but God has not changed.

FIRST LADY INVITEE (sermonizing):
-It is written "A Priest shall not marry a prostitute for he is a holy man of God. He must marry a virgin. He may not marry a widow, nor a woman who is divorced, nor a prostitute. She must be a virgin."

SECOND LADY INVITEE (opposes):
-But her would-be-husband is not a priest.

FIRST LADY INVITEE (approvingly):

-But everyone aspires to be a holy man of God. We do not have different laws for the priests and the other holy men of God.

SECOND LADY INVITEE (supports):

-Anyway, our 'in-charge' is now a 'born again'. She is entirely a brand-new creature; old things have passed away. That makes her a virgin and qualifies her for the wedding gown.

FIRST LADY INVITEE (blustering):

-The veil of the wedding gown will cover the multitude of abortions. That is theological extrapolation from mathematical juxtaposition in universal imposition.

(All the invitees in this vicinity are raptured in suppressed laughter. This lightens the mood in this circle of invitees)

That a woman who has delivered three times or aborted many times is a virgin.
If technology takes man to space and restores lost virginity, tell me, by what intelligence can virginal shyness be restored? Psychological restitution?

Let us wait and see what the 'ministers of the Lord' will decide. No one can tell where the pendulum will swing to or what the outcome will be.

(Attention is suddenly distracted by an argument between ROSE and the MINISTERS in the vestry)

FIRST MINISTER (to Rose, calmly):

-We have found out that you've been married before. Is that true?

ROSE (already fidgety):
-Yes! But I was the seventh wife of my former husband. And he did not treat me as a wife. So, I did quit.

SECOND MINISTER (coolly):
-Why didn't you furnish us with that information earlier?

ROSE:
-Since that marriage was formally ended, I did not see any relationship between it and this wedding.
THIRD MINISTER (composedly):
-I see! Can you give us some time to deliberate on this new finding?

(*Rose obligingly leaves the vestry. She is obviously restless and sad*)

FIRST MINISTER (collectedly):
-Why didn't she plan to have the wedding done in her hometown, the town of her place of work or her would-be-husband's, where her background is known? But she came here where no one knows her past.

SECOND MINISTER:
-That is how they deceive us into wedding pregnant girls, some of whom deliver three months after the marriage ceremony. This is a theological fraud.

(*BROTHER TITUS, who had been sent for, enters the vestry, already jittery*)

FIRST MINISTER (to BROTHER TITUS, sympathetically):

-The woman you intend to marry has been married before -expended already and is now a divorcee. Are you aware of these?

BROTHER TITUS:

-I know her very well.

THIRD MINISTER:

-For with whom you consort you become cohort, become one, sharing spirits, accusing demons, guilt and problems of their cohorts, partakers of their Fate, bound in their destinies, and bonded to their nemesis, for whom you follow determines what follows you. For these reasons what is prescribed for an untainted young man like you is a fresh, untapped virgin young girl. I hope you understand these mysteries fully.

BROTHER TITUS (firmly):

-I am aware of that. Then, she was in the world but now, a new creature. Old things have passed away. Everything about her has become brand new.

SECOND MINISTER (not sure whose sanity is still intact):

-And you still want to marry her? Note that she tasted marriage before, savoured its benefits, crucified it and now wants to be reconciled to marriage to crucify it a second time. Should she be given another opportunity to put that institution to shame again?

BROTHER TITUS:
-Yes! Because when she first got married, up to when she was divorced, she was of the world. But now she is 'born again', a brand-new creature!

THIRD MINISTER (soberly):
-Let me read the words to you.

(*Opens and reads*)

"And I tell you this, that anyone who divorces his wife, except for fornication, and marries another, commits adultery. And the man who marries a divorced woman commits adultery. Thou shall not commit adultery."

BROTHER TITUS (effusively):
-But the same scripture says: "Even if your sins are as black as charcoal, even though your sins are like scarlet, they'll be white like snow. Though they're like crimson, they'll become like wool once you repent.

(*While this discussion is still on, attention is suddenly focused on two male invitees whispering to each other, from among the people in the gathering. They are sitting near the rear window and so can see what is packed outside, just beside the church*)

SECOND MALE INVITEE (points out to his colleagues, excitedly):
-See, our 'in-charge' has bought a refrigerator, air-conditioner, television, video, fans, carpet, bed, chairs and other expensive household items.

THIRD MALE INVITEE (intones):

-Her would-be-husband is a very lucky man. His table has been prepared, laid with green pastures, his bread buttered, his nest feathered, his head has been anointed with oil by the gods and he shall never want.

SECOND MALE INVITEE (jokingly):

-If I saw a woman who would buy all these things into my house, I would marry her. I wouldn't give a hoot about what anyone says.

THIRD MALE INVITEE (surprised):

-Even if she is as old as our 'in-charge'?

SECOND MALE INVITEE:

-I would marry her. I wouldn't give a tinker's cuss about what anyone thinks. How old is she?

THIRD MALE INVITEE:

-She already has three children and has worked for about ten years. She's certainly not less than thirty-five years. Only made green and fresh by 'fertilizer'. Modern women are like tropical forest trees. Year in year out, they remain evergreen.

SECOND MALE INVITEE:

-Then she can still deliver a few more children. In this era of family planning, all one needs is two to three children.

THIRD MALE INVITEE:

-At about thirty-five, how many more years does she have for childbearing?

SECOND MALE INVITEE:
-The doctors say menopause starts about age forty-two.

THIRD MALE INVITEE:
-She still has about seven years. She may still be able to deliver three more babies.

SECOND MALE INVITEES:
-But they also say, near menopause there is relative infertility since most of the monthly periods are without the concomitant egg release.

THIRD MALE INVITEE:
-In other words, she might not even be lucky enough to deliver up to three times in this marriage.

SECOND MALE INVITEE:
-We haven't even taken into account other possible mishaps and ill-fated pregnancies that will have nothing to show for at the end.

THIRD MALE INVITEE:
-And who knows, she might be much older than thirty-five years. A spouse never really knows the exact age of his woman. He only takes what he is told.

SECOND MALE INVITEE:
-Well, if I marry this type of woman, not for anything else other than what she can bring into my family. After collecting all these expensive items, I will then marry another young girl, the genuine wife. While she becomes my special adviser.

THIRD INVITEE (warning him):
-Sure, she won't boss you around? Remember! He who pays the piper dictates the tune.

SIXTH INVITEE (stands up from his position in the gathering, interrupts)
-I cannot continue to waste my time here, I cannot wait here any longer. This wedding will not take place.

(*Exits*)

SEVENTH INVITEE (talks angrily as he leaves):
-Since noon till this late evening they are still undecided whether or not they will marry each other. If courtship is this turbulent, marriage life will be a war.
Divorce is certain tomorrow. Is this trial marriage by force?

(*Exits*)

FEW OTHER INVITEES (as they get going, variously):
-S-s-s-c-h, they want husband by all means. I must return home before it becomes too late. This one is divorce before marriage.

(*Exeunt*)

(*ROSE, sensing that her invitees will disperse in a moment, flings into the vestry. She is confused and restless*)

ROSEE:
-Respected ones, what have you decided concerning our wedding?

FIRST MINISTER (with some degree of finality):
-Hear this! (Opens the book and reads)
For married people, I have a command which is not my own but the Lord's. A wife must not leave her husband; but if she does, she must remain single or else be reconciled to her husband. And a husband must not divorce his wife.

ROSE (discomfited):
-I did that when I was in sin. But now I have repented my sins. Even the marriage was not a real one, I was the seventh wife.

SECOND MINISTER:
-We all follow the Lord's command.

ROSE (helplessly):
-The good Lord says: 'Even if your sins are as black as charcoal, once you've repented your sins, I will make your sins as white as snow. I will forgive you completely.
If the good Lord should forgive me of my sins, why should humans deny me of God's favour?

THIRD MINISTER (to other ministers):
-I think she has a point there. Her case is special. First, she was the seventh wife: was she really married? Then, she is now repented, 'born again ', restored, brand new.

FOURTH MINISTER (pensively):
-We should look into this case. This is a very special circumstance.

FIRST AND SECOND MINISTERS (variously, as they leave the vestry):

-I can only support and take part in what the Lord asks us to do. Remember: thou shall not add nor subtract from the word. There is only one way, one gospel, not another.

(*Exeunt*)

(*There is confusion. The FIRST AND SECOND MINIS-TERS, who disagreed with the other two, emerge from the vestry and take their exit. All the invitees are talking and grumbling about their wasted time at the same time*)

OTHER INVITEES (variously but alternately):

-Pshaw! A marriage that will never be! Women that will never marry! Females that will never become wives! Wonders will never, never end! Listen all ye daughters of Eve: a lesson for one is a lesson for all.

Mrs is not Bsc. that just any academy can award.

Husband is not a 'smile' that just any face can wear. Wedding gown is not 'Okrika' that just any woman can wear.

Eternity ring is not fashion ring that just any finger can wear.

Wedding bell is not the music that summons just any girl to dance.

Honour is not 'ice cream' that just any lips can lick. Crown is not a cap that just any head can wear.

Wife is not an appellation that just any woman can bear.

All because, marriage like heaven, places of rest are gated

and not opened to just any feet but to those for whom

they were prepared of the consensus of the spirit-kind Being a wife-material is not a gift that just any girl can receive.

For the brows of wives cannot be bought or worn by never-to-be wives.

But being a wife-material, like faith is a cultivatable art,

and being a wife is not taught in any varsity,

but a gift in the hands of the gods, like faith and eternal life:

all, gifts, given to whoever they will.
Some are destined to marry, some are not,
Some women are born to become wives, some are not,
according to the CONSENSUS of the gods.

(*Exeunt*)

(*This flusters ROSE. She runs from the vestry to the plat-form in front of the congregation to talk to the dispersing invitees. But their chatter is deafening. She cannot bring them under control. She flounces back to the vestry to try and convince the remaining Ministers but meets them as they emerge from the vestry. She confusedly accosts, al-ternately, first the emerging Ministers, then the dispers-ing invitees. Helpless, she stands on the platform and with arms akimbo and the bridal gown flung over her head*)

ROSE (aside, murmuring to herself):
-I thought I could prove the gods wrong, outsmart and beat them at their game and upturn their dominance.

(*Soliloquizes*)

What the gods have ordained is immutable and without remedy, and so has to be accepted.

I am only a victim of ineluctable fate.

For by similar cast and commission, sunrise is daily announced by cockcrow and sunset compels the rooster to retire, the earth spins on its axis and orbits the sun, and one season rolls into another; so are humas born, some appointed to fail, some commissioned to succeed, just as women are destined, some to marry and some to remain unmarried

as coded in their DNA sequence.

Yet, ultimately, all will die, with some souls fated to end in heaven and others in hell. The grains for the granary and the chaff for the fire,

by the consensus and pre-arrangement of the gods.

The humankind project, up to its ultimate evolved state, human perfection (indestructibility), the implanting of faithfulness in humans to engender immortality, like the clock, the seasons, dawn and dusk, life and death, being male or female, blessings and curses, karma: all has been set on autopilot by the pre-arrangement of the spirit-kind, that no human can change, just as none can boil the ocean.

The gods are to blame: they have sealed our fates, with imposed covenants and curses (do or die). Every step we take has been ordered by the gods, even before we were born.

The gods had foreordained that: wedding bell shall ring every time, wedding gown shall whirl in eddies of wind over every place, marriageable girls shall search everywhere, but not everything in skirts, not all nubile girls on earth shall ever be adorned with nuptial gowns.

Not every womb on Earth shall shelter babies

Not every nipple on Earth shall suckle babies

Not every woman on Earth shall have children

Not all humans on Earth shall live for ever

What we proposed or purposed is not set in stone. But what the gods assign us

is cast in stone.

The bread is in their hands, and the knife is in their hands to cut to their pleasure.

The clay is in their hands and pottery is their craft, designers of the pot.
The stone is at their disposal, sculptors of our destinies, as they set forth the armies of palmerworms, caterpillars, cankerworms and locust over unarmed hapless helpless humans.

They have cast in the stone that not all humans on earth will see paradise, not all the souls of men will enter heaven, not everything in skirts will have the honour of adornment with the wedding gown, not all beautiful girls on earth will ever be dignified with the lofty appellation: Mrs.

Not all women shall have husbands, become wives, become mothers nor know peace.

Mercy or destruction (wrath) has been reserved for them for whom it is prepared of the gods.

Just as they have destinated where, when and to whom we're born and when we will die, or who will live and who will die, and who is for Heaven and who is for Hell, the great commission.

The Dutch say: "The Devil sits behind the cross". For what purpose is this cooperation? Or why do they see this alliance? For the purposes of their teamwork: one sieves the grain into the granary and the other winnows the chaff into the fire. Oneness of purpose: collaborating for the sole purpose of separating good from evil, replicated by marriage, the separation of the married from the unmarried.

Our fates: birth, life, death, and sifting into store house or blowing into fire, once settled by the supreme spiritual council, their consensus is a done deal. Satan desired Peter as he did Judas I.

Jesus prayed for Peter who was sincere (had faith). Judas perished, Peter flourished: two sinners under the same saintly canopy: the canopy of faith, as with the two thieves at the crucifixion.

One with faith, the passport to heaven, and the other without faith, the passport to hell. The gods are to blame for fixing all at their whims and fancies.

(She is joined by BROTHER TITUS, who is as confused and helpless as she is. She puts her right hand in his)

(Aside)

-Don't blame the victims, commissioned script interpreters, merely playing their assigned roles, like a human, assigned without any choice, the role of either a man or a woman, the pawns on a chess board, the Xs and the Ys in the destiny equation.

Blame the victims' designs as set in place by the gods: their consensus, their pre-arrangements, their design is that

Mercy or destruction (wrath) has been reserved for them for whom it is prepared of the gods.

to prove the logic of superiority, the prerogative of dominance, the perks of power and confirm the law of supremacy or the role of servitude.

(Turns to Brother Titus):

-Don't mind these short-sighted people who cannot see beyond their nose. They have been used by the gods, to nail the destinies of humans.

They do not know that, for humans to attain immortality, they must be faithful to their creator; and for a woman to be protected from indiscriminate defilement, she must be faithful to a husband. As Israel survives annihilation amidst enemies because she depends on America, so will humans not be consumed by superior beings only if they depend on the supreme being to prove the law of freedom: freedom for the weak (woman) comes only from alignment (marriage) with the strongest (husband), her sanctuary of refuge,

married life, the prototype of eternal salvation.

So, you are my husband, my protector, my freedom made perfect, and I am your wife, your completeness. What we've put together, they cannot put asunder'. We are husband and wife, no schism, that is the way it's going to be: the design of the spirit-kind notwithstanding.

(In solidarity, RHAHAAB mounts the stage, joins TITUS and ROSE)

RHAHAAB (despondently):
-We are, just what we are: victims, pawns, vessels at their mercy and pleasure merely playing our assigned roles - flesh fed, fattened, and drilled on the stumbling block for the scheduled selection of compliant souls.
Our Conforming or being alignable or turning refractory is subject to their whims -we are nothing but the tools they make us to be; we are created raw-materials in their preprogrammed processing plant, 'life', that transforms or deforms us into whatever they had programmed us to be - lumps of clay for their pottery-work. We are what they intended us to be - what we were made for - malleable and convertible into processed products fit for either service to them or fuel for the fire, as they please.

Which of these can we call to order: weather, cloud, wind, destiny - but all are at their whims - just as we are.

313

Even the Sun, the Moon and all that are in the firmament dance to their ordinances, just as they have set in place.

Some, they cleanse into immortal beings, reflective of their image, its model, for us to learn from, is their transforming of some women into married (in-service) women,

the straw and the grain from the same seed, but the straw for incineration and the grain for the silos, an instantiation of salvation for the reformed, but destruction for the deformed or those refractory to reformation - as cast by the gods.

(ALICE and BEKI, looking stressed up, haggard, older, and unmarried, in solidarity also, mount the stage to join ROSE, RHAHAAB and TITUS)

(variously but alternately and bleakly)

-We are nothing but victims of the ominous curse of the gods.

Because womanity was desecrated before we were born, the gods, as

punishment ensure some women remain umarried or are childless.

RHAHAAB:
-And, unless women are under the protection of husbands, they are indiscriminately violated by all men - to convince

humans that unless they are under the wings of the supreme being, they will be devoured by the supramundane being - THE GRAND DESIGN to keep humankind burdened under the advancement of the purpose of the spirit-kind for which purpose the spirit-kind created humankind.

ALICE:

-The creator grants wives protection against indiscriminate attacks, harassment, humiliation and violations under their husbands as an instantiation people can see, experience God's type of protection and so learn to trust God to protect them from perishing (predators.) for if wives cannot submit to their husbands that they see, how can humans submit to God that they have not seen.

BEKI:

-Humans are assigned roles they choicelessly play (destiny) as concrete examples (constant reminders); by the parts we play, what we see or the experiences of our lives, we serve as Divine and demonic voices affirming and announcing the power of the spiritkind - which is the purpose of our creation, and lessons for others to learn from.

ALICE:

-And, as food processing plant processes food for human consumption so does Life process humans as tools for spiritual use.

BEKI:

-And, as industrial plant brings out products fit for human consumption, so is Life the preparation, the university, the processing plant that morphs humans into usable facet-specific vessels for one or the other side of the bi-faceted spirit-kind so that in perfection or in corruption, in heaven or in hell, in bliss or blast, humans are witnesses and announcers of the power of the spirit kind.

RHAHAAB:
-Life is the process of getting the grain and the chaff from the wheat for use by the two faces of the spirit-kind.

ALICE:
-Life is the milling process that sifts the grain from the chaff, separates the sheep from the goat, good from evil as shares for the two facets of the spirit-kind.

instantiated by the separation of women into married and unmarried women for use by husbands and violators - the caring and uncaring,

but both exploiting facets of the menfolk witnessing to the duality of our single destinal purpose: perfection and corruption or bliss and blast in heaven or hell proclaiming the POWER of the Highest.

ROSE:
-We are merely players or spectators or commentators of the twists and turns, high-octane thrills and spills in the cast of the scripts by the spirit-kind who revel in our pains and ride roughshod over us as they 'cruise' with their power over us.

We are not the spirits (lamb or lion - consuming fire) operating through us, (we are merely human agents). This is instantiated by the power of husbands over wives constantly witnessing to the power of the Highest.

TITUS:
-The spirit-kind made humankind to witness, appreciate and announce his power - even if he has to elevate one

(Moses) so the other will marvel at his Mercy or destroy one (Pharaoh) so that the one spared will marvel at his power.

One is born as babe, morphed by life into flawlessness or corruption; corruption to be destroyed and perfection to be preserved, all to showcase the power of the Highest.

Yes, the spirit kind is the source of humankind and so is justified to use his product in perfection or in corruption, by preservation (Israelites) or by destruction (Cananites) to showcase his power and advance his purpose just as the other is

born as a girl, morphed by life into a bride or an unmarriageable girl, both are used by men: bride as a wife (exclusively exploitated but preserved), the other, unmarriageable girl for defilement - indiscriminately defiled and exploited till destroyed,

both in advancement of the purpose of the husband and the violator, the facets of mankind, the physical example representing the spiritual setting for the Glory of the Highest.

So, whatever is thrust on you or however you

are used (married or unmarried, in perfection or

in corruption) - your allotment was set

before the foundation of the Earth.

If the lion licks you up or the lamb lifts you up,

Are the gods to blame? Remember!

317

The potter made the pot for his use.

Can you then blame the potter for using his pot?

More so, with all the warnings and real world

Examples of the result of ending as

PERFECTION OR CORRUPTION?

The Heavens, the moon, the angels and the creation in its entirety declare the Glory of the Highest - who are humans that the spirit-kind should be mindful of, to be used in any capacity, bent or wholesome is a crown of glory and honour - mere crafted image for showcasing the power of the spirit-kind. To be free is to live in awe of his power and only in Him is rest. Only in awe of his power shall Humans be free. Human freedom ends at the gate of the power of the spirit-kind.

ROSE (summarily):
-The cosmic set up (what has been pre-arranged) is that

women are made weaker so they will need protection from indiscriminate violations, harassment, humiliation and attacks by the male-kind, and

humans are made subpar so they will need protection from attacks, being taken over, controlled and used by the god-like kind,

that way, we all remain what we were made to be:

tools in the hands of the spirit-kind.

318

Each person a narrator of some aspects of the diverse powers of the spirit-kind.

Each life a participant in the evangelism of the infinite powers of the spirit-kind.

All, together, choicelessly compulsory, used as mere witnesses and campaigners of the aura of the omnipotence of the spirit-kind - wherein lies the freedom of humankind -

in the self-same secret places in which are hidden riches and treasures of darkness, the abode of refuge, and safety, in the intimate relationship, the secret place, the secret that is hidden from the opposing camp.

The cosmic purpose for this threesome game is that

The god-like kind and the Highest kind

toss humankind about allowing the intelligent life, the conscious entity to wake up the entire universal entities to give cosmic harmony.

Curtain falls.

EPILOGUE TO HUMANS SHALL BE FREE
(SOVEREIGN POWER)

A THREE-YEAR-OLD GIRL (To her mother):
-Mom. if God sends you, go oooh! If you don't, re-member Jonah.

MOTHER (of the said three-year-old girl):
-What happened to Jonah?

THE THREE-YEAR-OLD GIRL:
-God sent Jonah to go and preach in Nineveh. He re-fused and ran into a ship. God picked him from the ship, threw him into the sea and a big fish swallowed him.

THE END

Contents

Finito di stampare
nel mese di novembre 2023
presso Rotomail Italia S.p.A. – Vignate (MI)